THE ASC
OF A LEA
EXPERIENCE GUIDE

For use with the book
The Ascent of a Leader

Developing High Trust Leaders™

HOW ORDINARY RELATIONSHIPS
DEVELOP EXTRAORDINARY
CHARACTER & INFLUENCE

Other Resources by
Bill Thrall and Bruce McNicol

The Ascent of a Leader

TrueFaced Experience Edition
(with John Lynch)

TrueFaced Experience Guide
(with John Lynch)

TrueFaced Experience 2-DVD set
(with John Lynch)

Beyond Your Best
(with John Lynch)

Affirmation for your Marriage

Affirmation for your Family

THE ASCENT
OF A LEADER
EXPERIENCE GUIDE

For use with the book
The Ascent of a Leader

HOW ORDINARY RELATIONSHIPS
DEVELOP EXTRAORDINARY
CHARACTER & INFLUENCE

Bill Thrall and Bruce McNicol

Contributors: John Lynch, Ken McElrath, Mark Carver, Amanda Smith,
Judy Gomoll and Julie Thrush

LEADERSHIP
CATALYST

A Leadership Catalyst Resource
www.leadershipcatalyst.org

Leadership Catalyst, Inc.
1600 E. Northern Avenue, Suite 280, Phoenix, AZ 85020
Toll free - 1.888.249.0700 www.leadershipcatalyst.org

Established in 1995, Leadership Catalyst is an international resource for helping people learn how to build and restore trust in their key relationships. Through this resource many people experience remarkable communities of authenticity, safety, maturity and productivity. These communities are often described by the phrase, "environments of grace."

The vision of Leadership Catalyst is to leave in its wake thousands of trust-building, truth-telling environments of grace. The mission of Leadership Catalyst is to build and restore trust in your key relationships.

The Catalyst Trust Model ™ is a modular, systematic approach to forming and reproducing High-Trust Leaders™ and High Trust Cultures™. Built on rock-solid biblical principles and rising from more than 75 years of combined leadership experience, *The Catalyst Trust Model* ™ provides a unique experience with positive change.

Leadership Catalyst Resources are available through our website. Substantial discounts on bulk quantities of LCI resources are available to corporations, professional associations, and other organizations. For details and discount information, contact Leadership Catalyst at 1.888. 249.0700, or visit our website at www.leadershipcatalyst.org

**LEADERSHIP
CATALYST**

ISBN 0-9770908-0-9

Printed in the United States of America

Authors: William A. Thrall and Bruce McNicol

To all those in the wake of your influence

Thanks to the staff and families at Leadership Catalyst who are enjoying the wonder of these principles at an increasing level in their relationships with Jesus, the staff, and their families and friends.

Bill Thrall and Bruce McNicol

TABLE OF CONTENTS

INTRODUCTION

The Ascent of a Leader Experience Guide

Welcome! You have decided to begin *The Ascent of a Leader Experience.*

This Experience Guide was created to guide you through the principles found in the book *The Ascent of a Leader.* This guide is not designed to be a stand-alone workbook, but part of an interactive experience that your small group, mentoring relationships, ministry teams and Sunday school classes can use to cultivate extraordinary character and influence.

The highly interactive and relationship-focused Tools contained in this work-book will put flesh on the principles found in *The Ascent of a Leader*, breathing new life into you and your relationships.

To get the most out of your time, you need to be committed to three things:

▶ *Bring a positive, adventurous spirit with you into the training.* Leadership Catalyst has spent thousands of hours preparing this process, but your attitude and energy will be the deciding factor for success in this transforming mission. Most of the content is built around carefully designed team exercises. Your enthusiastic participation is critical to launching this process well.

▶ *Allow the material to penetrate your heart as you process it with your team in the follow-up sessions.* Relationships will strengthen as each of you learn how to ignite and fan the flames of trust, bringing powerful positive change and growth to you and your organization.

▶ *Remember that the initial training is just the first step in an ongoing trust-building process. The Ascent of a Leader* introduces you to the Seven Essential Principles of the high-trust culture and the Ladder of Influence. But this is just the beginning. Personal, relational and environ-mental changes take time, energy and yes, faith. Trust is square one. The initial training is just the beginning of the adventure. Where it goes is up to you!

If you are not part of a team that is processing this material, but want to find out how you and your team could receive additional resources, contact Leadership Catalyst at 1-888-249-0700 or visit our website at www.leadershipcatalyst.org.

Enjoy the adventure of creating a trust-building culture together!

THE CAPACITY LADDER

Attain Individual Potential

Acquire Title or Position

Develop My Capacities

Discover What I Can Do

THE INTEGRATED LADDER

Destiny

Attain God-designed Potential

Suffering

Acquire Positions that Match Who I Am

Obedience

Develop My True Capacities in Team

Submission

Discover What I Can Do with God & Others

Humility

RELATIONSHIPS OF TRUST   ENVIRONMENTS OF GRACE

THE CHARACTER LADDER

Destiny

Suffering

Obedience

Submission

Humility

RELATIONSHIPS OF TRUST   ENVIRONMENTS OF GRACE

Welcome to the first session of The Ascent of a Leader Experience.

Session One:

Character and Capacity

The first part of each session - Experiencing The Ascent of a Leader on Your Own - includes a number of specific questions based on the related content in *The Ascent of a Leader* book. Take time to read the assigned book chapter, passages from the Bible, and to go through each question on your own. Use the space provided in the Experience Guide to record your thoughts, concerns, questions, and insights.

The second part - Experiencing The Ascent of a Leader Together - is a group experience that expands on the concepts you explored on your own and makes them come alive through creative, focused, and field tested activities. Meet with your group to go through these activities and plan on 30-40 minutes to complete them each session.

1
CHARACTER
& CAPACITY

Experiencing The Ascent of a Leader on Your Own

PERSONAL PREP

Character and Capacity

1 Read Chapters One and Two in *The Ascent of a Leader* and Philippians 2:5-11. Take time to soak up all the stories and thoughts. This will be the basis for answering the following questions. You may want to review the "Grabbing Hold" questions at the end of the chapter in *The Ascent of a Leader* as well.

2 Get out a pen or pencil and respond to the "Grabbing Hold" questions that follow. Keep in mind this is your personal workbook for examining the truths in *The Ascent of a Leader* and selected passages from the Bible.

GRABBING HOLD

Character and Capacity

"This book is for those who want their influence to make a positive difference, in whatever sphere of influence God has granted them. It is for those who wish to explore a better course--one that addresses their inner longings for purpose and meaning. [It] beckons you to embrace a lifelong adventure of self-discovery and to couple this adventure with interdependent relationships and perennial pursuit of God. [It] calls you to create and live within safe environments that awaken and nurture the purposes God has for you and the people around you." (page 11, *The Ascent of a Leader*)

1. Before you launch into the adventure of ascending and climbing, let's pause to consider realistically where you are right now. Describe in a few phrases or sentences the current reality in/of:

▶ your sphere of influence (Who is in the wake of your influence? How's it going?)

▶ your inner longing for purpose and meaning (How satisfied are you?)

▶ your on-going self-discovery (Where is the cutting edge of your personal and interpersonal growth?)

▶ your interdependent relationships (In your various contexts, with whom are you experiencing an invigorating sense of team? How much are you trusting others with you?)

▶ your perennial pursuit of God (How much are you trusting God with you?)

▶ your safe environments (Who--if anyone--provides a safe environment for you? How are you providing safety for those you influence?)

Has this bit of introspection surfaced any hints of a below-the-waterline issue in your life that might negatively impact your legacy as a leader if it isn't addressed? Explain.

2. Think of gifted leaders who have fallen or finished poorly. (Note: Be gracious here and do not write or share names.) What do you think hindered such capable leaders in the process of their character development?

3. What life experiences stimulated the most growth in your character? Who was influencing your life at the time?

4. What happens to the leader when there is a disconnect between "being" and "doing"? What happens to the followers?

TRUSTING TRUTH
Character and Capacity

5. Jesus' hand-picked leaders ultimately revealed their desire to aspire to the top rung in Luke 9:46-48. What do you think the disciples missed and why? What do you think is causing Christian leaders today to miss the point?

Experiencing The Ascent of a Leader Together

Before you begin:

1. Get together with your group. If you are a part of a large group (such as a church or school class), your teacher or leader will facilitate the experience. If you're doing this in a small-group setting, anyone can lead the group. If you are the small group leader, review the Leader Guidelines in the Leader's Section on page 118 in the back of this guide.

2. Consider the following guidelines for making the most of your group experience:

▶ When you are directed to form a small group for an activity, *select people you know at least a little.* If you are placed in a pair or trio with people you don't know, take a couple minutes to introduce yourselves. This will give you a good starting place for today's experiential activity.

▶ *Follow the directions carefully,* particularly as they relate to discussion in your small group. These directions have been designed to provide safe boundaries so you can share appropriately with others.

▶ The skills, techniques, and truths you discover during this experience are applicable in many other areas of life. *Practice what you learn outside of this small-group time.*

▶ Above all, *don't be anxious about the experiential activities in this guide.* They aren't scary, "stand up in front of the group and share your life" experiences. Each "Experiencing The Ascent of a Leader Together" activity has been field-tested and is designed to ease you into participation. That's not to say what you learn will be fluffy, surface-level stuff. The experiences can be life-changing. We'll lead you into the deeper stuff. But come prepared to invest yourself in the experience. It will be worth it.

Experiencing The Ascent of a Leader Together

CHARACTER AND CAPACITY

Welcome

Take a moment to greet one another. If you traditionally enjoy snacks with your group, have at 'em. Use the opening moments as people congregate for a brief time of fellowship.

Small Group Experience

We have selected a few questions from the "Experiencing The Ascent of a Leader on Your Own" section to discuss as a team. Take a few minutes and discuss your responses with your small group. After your discussion, continue your experience with the small group exercise on the following page.

1. What life experiences stimulated the most growth in your character? Who was influencing your life at the time?

2. What happens to the leader when there is a disconnect between "being" and "doing"? What happens to the followers?

FACING EXPECTATIONS

LEADERSHIP
CATALYST

Please do not duplicate
To order this tool visit
www.leadershipcatalyst.org
Phone: 888.249.0700

PERSONAL PREP

1 Begin by forming a small group with one or two partners. Groups of three work best. This experience should take approximately 30 minutes.

2 On the *Facing Expectations* worksheet, in the first column entitled "Unmet Expectation," identify one personal example of a disintegrated leader who violated your expectations. This example should be from a previous team experience and not an example involving a person in this small group. Explain the situation and what you expected. A sample of a completed *Facing Expectations* worksheet is provided on the next page to help you.

3 In the second column, entitled "The Pain of Disintegration," describe your feelings when you realized that your expectation would not be realized.

4 In the third column, entitled "My Reaction," describe your attitude or actions following the unmet expectation. Did you do anything in response to those who failed to meet your expectation?

A TIME FOR US

1 Share your experiences from the *Facing Expectations* worksheet with each other.

2 With your team member, listen carefully to each other as you share, noting disappointments, feelings expressed and reactions.

3 After you have both finished, discuss the following questions, noting your answers on the *Expectation Resolution* worksheet:
• How could the disappointments and reactions have been avoided?
• How can the disappointments and reactions be resolved?

For an Enjoyable Experience

Bring a mindset that says, "I am for the other person's best."

Allow other group members to answer their questions.

Allow other group members to "keep" their answers. Do not correct.

Allow other group members to share their answers. Do not counsel. Listening to others talk about their experience is a wonderful affirmation for them.

Allow other group members to experience safety. Do not discuss their answers outside your group, unless they give you permission to do so.

---

1 CHARACTER & CAPACITY

FACING EXPECTATIONS Sample Worksheet

UNMET EXPECTATION	THE PAIN OF DISINTEGRATION	MY REACTION
In the name of busyness, pressure of role, signifi-cance of responsibilities - a leader broke multi-ple commitments to me. He con-stantly wanted to center on his over-all contributions, rather than his affect on me.	I initially aspired to be like this leader. I felt the pain of betrayal and a con-stant sense of being demeaned.	I lost confidence in his integrity and respect for his person. I withdrew. I found and relat-ed with others he dealt with similarly. I protected myself and did my job until I found another. We never did resolve.

LEADERSHIP CATALYST

Please do not duplicate
To order this tool visit
www.leadershipcatalyst.org
Phone: 888.249.0700

FACING EXPECTATIONS Worksheet

UNMET EXPECTATION	THE PAIN OF DISINTEGRATION	MY REACTION

LEADERSHIP CATALYST

Please do not duplicate
To order this tool visit
www.leadershipcatalyst.org
Phone: 888.249.0700

CHARACTER & CAPACITY

EXPECTATION RESOLUTION Worksheet

How could the pain and reactions have been avoided?

How can the pain and reactions be resolved?

LEADERSHIP
CATALYST

Please do not duplicate
To order this tool visit
www.leadershipcatalyst.org
Phone: 888.249.0700

PROCESSING THE FACING EXPECTATIONS EXPERIENCE

Form one large group and discuss the following question for no more than three minutes: What did you experience? Allow time for everyone who so desires to respond. Stay focused on the processing question and use the guidelines outlined previously to facilitate a healthy discussion.

CLOSING PRAYER

After exploring the processing question together, close in prayer and review the homework for the next session (see below).

BEFORE THE NEXT SESSION

Read Chapter Three in *The Ascent of a Leader*. Then complete the "Experiencing The Ascent of a Leader on Your Own" section for session two that follows. Pray throughout the week that your discoveries will positively impact all aspects of your everyday life.

**THE
INTEGRATED
LADDER**

Welcome to Session Two of The Ascent of a Leader Experience.

Session Two:

Environments of Grace

The first part of each session - Experiencing The Ascent of a Leader on Your Own - includes a number of specific questions based on the related content in *The Ascent of a Leader* book. Take time to read the assigned book chapter, passages from the Bible, and to go through each question on your own. Use the space provided in the Experience Guide to record your thoughts, concerns, questions, and insights.

The second part - Experiencing The Ascent of a Leader Together - is a group experience that expands on the concepts you explored on your own and makes them come alive through creative, focused, and field tested activities. Meet with your group to go through these activities and plan on 30-40 minutes to complete them each session.

Experiencing The Ascent of a Leader on Your Own

PERSONAL PREP

Environments of Grace

1 Read Chapter Three in *The Ascent of a Leader* and Philippians 2:5-11. Take time to soak up all the stories and thoughts. This will be the basis for answering the following questions. You may want to review the "Grabbing Hold" questions at the end of the chapter in *The Ascent of a Leader* as well.

2 Get out a pen or pencil and respond to the "Grabbing Hold" questions that follow. Keep in mind this is your personal workbook for examining the truths in *The Ascent of a Leader* and selected passages from the Bible.

GRABBING HOLD

Environments of Grace

"...'one could argue that the only thing of real importance that leaders do is create and manage culture, and the unique talent of leaders is their ability to understand and work with culture.' The ability to initiate and sustain positive cultural change may prove to be the single greatest need of twenty-first century organizations... Positive cultural change means removing the barriers between what is good within our own souls and what is good within the soul of the cultures we live in...

　　When leaders create an atmosphere of care and concern, hope and vision flourish. The seeds of destiny in their followers begin to crack through their shells as leaders encourage each person with the prospect of becoming all they were intended to be." (pages 26-27, 39, *The Ascent of a Leader*)

1. Do you know or have you experienced an environment (or culture) of grace? Perhaps you felt it around a mentor, at home, at church, or on a work team. Describe the impact it had on you.

The authors often make this statement, "How I view myself is the most revealing commentary of my theology."(see Page 65, *TrueFaced Experience Edition*, NavPress 2004)

Sometimes there is a hidden discrepancy between what we believe God will do for others and what we actually trust Him to do for us. Sometimes we can give incredible accurate theological statements regarding who God is, and it seems to have so little effect on who we are in our relationship with Him.

Sometimes we can give incredible belief statements regarding who God says we are, and yet who we believe we are is so incredibly disconnected.

2. How do safe (not soft) environments shape character?

3. Try to assess the current environmental conditions in your context (where you work, live, worship, or serve). Check any that you think apply:

Environments of Grace:
___ We feel safe
___ We grow up
___ We trust each other
___ We live authentically
___ We celebrate each other

Environments of Grace: (Continued)
___ We laugh a lot
___ We produce better
___ We're more creative
___ We're free to be who we are
___ We dream of possibilities
___ We take risks
___ (Others?)

Environments of Ungrace:
___ We fear being belittled or marginalized
___ We must earn favor and love
___ We distrust each other
___ We feel isolated and independent
___ We experience conflict between groups or people
___ We hide our faults and weaknesses
___ We pretend we don't have faults and weaknesses
___ Our problem-solving decreases
___ Rigidity and policies drive us
___ We play it safe to avoid risk
___ We have a distorted view of reality
___ (Others?)

How are the items you checked affecting who you are, how you relate to others, and even to God?

TRUSTING TRUTH

Environments of Grace

4. Read John 4:4-30. Review the elements of an environment of grace that the woman at the well experienced with Jesus. Choose just two and describe how your commitment to implementing these elements could increase the level of grace and emotional safety in your environment. How are the items you checked affecting who you are, how you relate to others, and even to God?

Experiencing The Ascent of a Leader Together

Before you begin:

1. Get together with your group. If you are a part of a large group (such as a church or school class), your teacher or leader will facilitate the experience. If you're doing this in a small-group setting, anyone can lead the group. If you are the small group leader, review the Leader Guidelines in the Leader's Section on page 118 in the back of this guide.

2. Consider the following guidelines for making the most of your group experience:

▶ When you are directed to form a small group for an activity, *select people you know at least a little.* If you are placed in a pair or trio with people you don't know, take a couple minutes to introduce yourselves. This will give you a good starting place for today's experiential activity.

▶ *Follow the directions carefully*, particularly as they relate to discussion in your small group. These directions have been designed to provide safe boundaries so you can share appropriately with others.

▶ The skills, techniques, and truths you discover during this experience are applicable in many other areas of life. *Practice what you learn outside of this small-group time.*

▶ Above all, *don't be anxious about the experiential activities in this guide.* They aren't scary, "stand up in front of the group and share your life" experiences. Each "Experiencing The Ascent of a Leader Together" activity has been field-tested and is designed to ease you into participation. That's not to say what you learn will be fluffy, surface-level stuff. The experiences can be life-changing. We'll lead you into the deeper stuff. But come prepared to invest yourself in the experience. It will be worth it.

2 ENVIRONMENTS OF GRACE

ENVIRONMENTS OF GRACE

Welcome

Take a moment to greet one another. If you traditionally enjoy snacks with your group, have at 'em. Use the opening moments as people congregate for a brief time of fellowship.

Small Group Experience

We have selected a few questions from the "Experiencing The Ascent of a Leader on Your Own" section to discuss as a team. Take a few minutes and discuss your responses with your small group. After your discussion, continue your experience with the small group exercise on the following page.

1. How do "safe" (not soft) environments shape character?

2. Review the elements of an environment of grace that the woman at the well experienced with Jesus in John 4:4-30. (These elements are on page 25-26 of this guide.) Choose just two and describe how your commitment to implementing these elements could increase the level of grace and emotional safety in your environment. How are the items you checked affecting who you are, how you relate to others, and even to God?

AM I EXPERIENCING ACCEPTANCE?

LEADERSHIP
CATALYST

PERSONAL PREP

Please do not duplicate
To order this tool visit
www.leadershipcatalyst.org
Phone: 888.249.0700

1 Begin by forming a small group with one or two partners. Groups of three work best. This experience should take approximately 30 minutes.

2 On the *Am I Experiencing Acceptance?* worksheet, answer each question by circling the number below the answer that best describes how you feel (Strongly Agree, Agree, Unsure or Maybe, Disagree or Strongly Disagree). Complete this for how you feel in relation to God, your family while growing up, and a past team.

3 When you've finished, add up the circled numbers in each section and write the total in the proper box. When you are through, you should have three separate scores, each ranging between 7 and 35.

4 Turn to the Experience Analysis on page 32 to interpret your scores and then complete the Processing Questions on page 31 to prepare for your next team discussion.

5 When you have completed the Experience Analysis, meet together as a team and complete the A Time For Us process on page 33.

For an Enjoyable Experience

Bring a mindset that says, "I am for the other person's best."

Allow other group members to answer their questions.

Allow other group members to "keep" their answers. Do not correct.

Allow other group members to share their answers. Do not counsel. Listening to others talk about their experience is a wonderful affirmation for them.

Allow other group members to experience safety. Do not discuss their answers outside your group, unless they give you permission to do so.

AM I EXPERIENCING ACCEPTANCE?
Worksheet

2 ENVIRONMENTS OF GRACE

From God?	STRONGLY AGREE	AGREE	UNSURE OR MAYBE	DISAGREE	STRONGLY DISAGREE
1. I think when God looks at me, he smiles.	5	4	3	2	1
2. I feel reluctant or ashamed to ask God to do things for me or meet my needs.	1	2	3	4	5
3. I am afraid of messing up God's plan for my life.	1	2	3	4	5
4. When I worship, work or pray, I feel content, adequate and worthy before God.	5	4	3	2	1
5. I feel free to express a full range of emotions to God, even anger and disappointment.	5	4	3	2	1
6. I feel like God is dissatisfied with my performance or level of sacrifice and service.	1	2	3	4	5
7. I talk to God frequently and naturally as if talking things over with a dear friend.	5	4	3	2	1

TOTAL OF ALL THE NUMBERS CIRCLED = [   ]

From my family while growing up?	STRONGLY AGREE	AGREE	UNSURE OR MAYBE	DISAGREE	STRONGLY DISAGREE
1. I felt free and safe enough to admit my mistakes to my family.	5	4	3	2	1
2. I felt I had to defend my choices, feelings and actions when around them.	1	2	3	4	5
3. My wants, likes, dislikes and values were respected and honored by them.	5	4	3	2	1
4. I could ask for my needs to be met without belittlement.	5	4	3	2	1
5. I was free to be inconsistent or illogical with them.	5	4	3	2	1
6. I could always express my fears to them and be heard.	5	4	3	2	1
7. I rarely cried in front of them or with them.	1	2	3	4	5

TOTAL OF ALL THE NUMBERS CIRCLED = [   ]

LEADERSHIP CATALYST

Please do not duplicate
To order this tool visit
www.leadershipcatalyst.org
Phone: 888.249.0700

From a previous team?	STRONGLY AGREE	AGREE	UNSURE OR MAYBE	DISAGREE	STRONGLY DISAGREE
1. I felt what I contributed was more important than who I was.	1	2	3	4	5
2. I felt the freedom to laugh.	5	4	3	2	1
3. I felt guarded rather than appreciated.	1	2	3	4	5
4. We openly expressed and experienced affirmation.	5	4	3	2	1
5. I felt the need to conform.	1	2	3	4	5
6. My point of view was heard.	5	4	3	2	1
7. I needed my team.	5	4	3	2	1

TOTAL OF ALL THE NUMBERS CIRCLED = [   ]

PROCESSING QUESTIONS

Based on what you learned from this experience and the Experience Analysis on page 32, answer the following questions:

1. *In which area is it easiest for you to experience acceptance?*

_____

_____

_____

_____

_____

2. *Are there any statements in the Experience Analysis section that stand out to you?*

_____

_____

_____

_____

_____

3. *Select one insight from this assignment to share with your team.*

_____

_____

_____

_____

_____

LEADERSHIP
CATALYST

Please do not duplicate
To order this tool visit
www.leadershipcatalyst.org
Phone: 888.249.0700

AM I EXPERIENCING ACCEPTANCE?

Analysis

Score Interpretations

In any area, experiencing acceptance from God, from your family, or from your team, the following interpretations apply:

Score Range	Interpretation
29-35	You feel very accepted in this relationship. Your sense of acceptance overflows into the lives of others. It may even be contagious. People sense your confidence and wonder at its source. You probably have a great deal of confidence in the rightness or acceptability of your choices.
22-28	You feel accepted in this relationship, but sometimes waffle. You have more good days than bad days. Most of the time, you have enough confidence to overcome your occasional doubts about yourself. You believe in the acceptance offered to you through this relationship, but still are affected by doubts for some reason.
14-21	You feel unaccepted in this relationship. You have more bad days than good ones. When faced with doubts about yourself, you tend to believe, unconsciously or consciously, that you don't deserve acceptance or don't need it. You are in danger because your lack of fulfillment in this area could lead you into unhealthy choices. You probably have been offered acceptance but may need to work through issues of trust in order to receive it well.
Less than 14	You are feeling a strong lack of acceptance in this relationship. This may be due to actual or perceived mistreatment or even severe abuse. It may also be the result of extreme personal resistance to receiving the love of others. You cannot move forward in health unless you ask others for focused help and receive it. Aware or not, you will seek acceptance from some other source, healthy or unhealthy, in order to have this need met. It would be wise to evaluate our choices now to ensure the choices you are making are healthy one.

LEADERSHIP
CATALYST

Please do not duplicate
To order this tool visit
www.leadershipcatalyst.org
Phone: 888.249.0700

A TIME FOR US

ENVIRONMENTS OF GRACE **2**

Purpose: To practice sharing who you are and how you feel with your team members, and to practice listening to the same from your team members.

At your team meeting, be prepared to share your thoughts about the items below. Remember to be sensitive to others, not letting any one person dominate the discussion.

1 As you process the *Am I Experiencing Acceptance?* Experience with your team, be affirming and accepting. Listen carefully and don't be tempted to jump in to fix things. The issues this Tool may raise could be very painful for some. Be patient. Don't play psychologist if issues arise. The most significant thing you can do is try to understand what you're feeling or what others are saying. The process is valuable because it will raise your awareness of how your team approaches life and relationships. This knowledge will help your team purposefully reshape your relationships to reflect acceptance and grace, creating a context for healing to take place over time.

2 *Discuss the following questions together:*

- ▶ *Did you find the* Am I Experiencing Acceptance? *Experience to be helpful?*

- ▶ *How do you think your family's acceptance of you while you were growing up affects your feelings of acceptance by God?*

- ▶ *How do you think your feelings about God or family affect how you're feeling toward your present team, your community or other organizations?*

- ▶ *Do you often communicate acceptance to your family, friends or peers on your team? If so, share some specific examples. If not, what prevents you?*

- ▶ *From what we have discovered so far in this journey, how do you think a greater level of acceptance could impact our team?*

- ▶ *In our organization, what could we do to foster a greater level of acceptance and grace in our relationships?*

- ▶ *What questions do we have as a team in the area of practically applying principles of acceptance?*

LEADERSHIP
CATALYST

2 BNVIRONMENTS OF GRACE

PROCESSING THE AM I EXPERIENCING ACCEPTANCE? EXPERIENCE

Form one large group and discuss the following question for no more than three minutes: What did you experience? Allow time for everyone who so desires to respond. Stay focused on the processing question and use the guidelines outlined previously to facilitate a healthy discussion.

CLOSING PRAYER

After exploring the processing question together, close in prayer and review the homework for the next session (see below).

BEFORE THE NEXT SESSION

Read Chapter Four in *The Ascent of a Leader*. Then complete the "Experiencing The Ascent of a Leader on Your Own" section for session three that follows. Pray throughout the week that your discoveries will positively impact all aspects of your everyday life.

NOTES

THE INTEGRATED LADDER

Welcome to Session Three of The Ascent of a Leader Experience.

Session Three:

Relationships of Trust

The first part of each session - <u>Experiencing The Ascent of a Leader on Your Own</u> - includes a number of specific questions based on the related content in *The Ascent of a Leader* book. Take time to read the assigned book chapter, passages from the Bible, and to go through each question on your own. Use the space provided in the Experience Guide to record your thoughts, concerns, questions, and insights.

The second part - <u>Experiencing The Ascent of a Leader Together</u> - is a group experience that expands on the concepts you explored on your own and makes them come alive through creative, focused, and field tested activities. Meet with your group to go through these activities and plan on 30-40 minutes to complete them each session.

Experiencing The Ascent of a Leader on Your Own

PERSONAL PREP
Relationships of Trust

1 Read Chapter Four in *The Ascent of a Leader* and Philippians 2:5-11. Take time to soak up all the stories and thoughts. This will be the basis for answering the following questions. You may want to review the "Grabbing Hold" questions at the end of the chapter in *The Ascent of a Leader* as well.

2 Get out a pen or pencil and respond to the "Grabbing Hold" questions that follow. Keep in mind this is your personal workbook for examining the truths in *The Ascent of a Leader* and selected passages from the Bible.

GRABBING HOLD
Relationships of Trust

1. We worship a Triune God whose three Persons--Father, Son and Holy Spirit--perpetually inter-relate among themselves. So when God said, "Let us make man in our image, in our likeness. . ." it followed that humankind was designed to inter-relate. We can't help it! We are "wired" for relationships! Do you believe that God the Father, Son, and Holy Spirit live in a mutual dependency? If so, how? What does this reveal/imply about how we are created in God's image?

"Every one of us has needs that can only be met by God and others. A need is anything we require or lack, in order to be fulfilled and productive . . . We have needs for significance, for protection, for security, and for provision. And there are many others. Because these needs may seem so 'soft,' they may not attract attention. But when we deny our God-given needs, try to meet them on our own, or demand that others fill them on our terms, we will not experience fulfillment. Without fulfillment-- the realization of our abilities and potential--we will not only accomplish less, but will also fall far short of the greater purposes of our lives." (page 44, *The Ascent of a Leader*)

2. Which is harder for you; to love others or to let them love you? Why?

3. Name someone whom you trust. What characteristics does this person possess that elicit trust from you?

4. What happens to relationships when they are based on performance? What happens to you?

TRUSTING TRUTH
Relationships of Trust

5. The apostle Paul was fluent in the love language of affirmation, as we see in the way he closes many of his letters. Read II Timothy 1:3-14. What effect do you believe Paul's words of loving affirmation had on his relationship with Timothy? What effect did it have on the value of trust in that relationship?

6. Were you affirmed growing up? What impact did it have on your sense of identity and value? Who has affirmed you in a way that you appreciated? What qualities helped you receive their affirmation?

Experiencing The Ascent of a Leader Together

Before you begin:

1. Get together with your group. If you are a part of a large group (such as a church or school class), your teacher or leader will facilitate the experience. If you're doing this in a small-group setting, anyone can lead the group. If you are the small group leader, review the Leader Guidelines in the Leader's Section on page 118 in the back of this guide.

2. Consider the following guidelines for making the most of your group experience:

    ▶ When you are directed to form a small group for an activity, *select people you know at least a little.* If you are placed in a pair or trio with people you don't know, take a couple minutes to introduce yourselves. This will give you a good starting place for today's experiential activity.

    ▶ *Follow the directions carefully,* particularly as they relate to discussion in your small group. These directions have been designed to provide safe boundaries so you can share appropriately with others.

    ▶ The skills, techniques, and truths you discover during this experience are applicable in many other areas of life. *Practice what you learn outside of this small-group time.*

    ▶ Above all, *don't be anxious about the experiential activities in this guide.* They aren't scary, "stand up in front of the group and share your life" experiences. Each "Experiencing The Ascent of a Leader Together" activity has been field-tested and is designed to ease you into participation. That's not to say what you learn will be fluffy, surface-level stuff. The experiences can be life-changing. We'll lead you into the deeper stuff. But come prepared to invest yourself in the experience. It will be worth it.

Experiencing The Ascent of a Leader Together

RELATIONSHIPS OF TRUST

Welcome

Take a moment to greet one another. If you traditionally enjoy snacks with your group, have at 'em. Use the opening moments as people congregate for a brief time of fellowship.

Small Group Experience

We have selected a few questions from the "Experiencing The Ascent of a Leader on Your Own" section to discuss as a team. Take a few minutes and discuss your responses with your small group. After your discussion, continue your experience with the small group exercise on the following page.

1. Name someone whom you trust. What characteristics does this person possess that elicit trust from you?

2. What happens to relationships when they are based on performance? What happens to you?

AFFIRMING EACH OTHER

LEADERSHIP
CATALYST

Please do not duplicate
To order this tool visit
www.leadershipcatalyst.org
Phone: 888.249.0700

PERSONAL PREP

1 Begin by forming a small group with one or two partners. Groups of three work best. This experience should take approximately 30 minutes. (A sample of a completed *Affirming You* worksheet is provided on the next page to help you.)

2 At the top of the *Affirming You* worksheet on page 46, write the name of the one you are affirming in the space provided. (One Affirming You worksheet is provided in this guide. You may make copies for those in your group that have *The Ascent of a Leader Experience Guide.*)

3 Circle all the words or phrases you believe to be true about this person.

4 Write the top five words or phrases—those you think best describe your friend—in the box provided. Jot down any notes about examples that will reinforce your thoughts.

A TIME FOR US

1 Share your top five answers from the *Affirming You* worksheet with your friend, reinforcing your affirmations with examples from your life, encouragement and appreciation whenever possible. When you are on the receiving end of the exercise, record what you hear on the *What I Heard About Me* worksheet and ***please take no time to counter what is said.*** This is the other person's opportunity to share his/her perspective on you. No negative statements or disagreement are allowed. Instead, listen intently and focus on letting it soak in. As time permits, share other items you circled from the *Affirming You* worksheet.

For an Enjoyable Experience

Bring a mindset that says, "I am for the other person's best."

Allow other group members to answer their questions.

Allow other group members to "keep" their answers. Do not correct.

Allow other group members to share their answers. Do not counsel. Listening to others talk about their experience is a wonderful affirmation for them.

Allow other group members to experience safety. Do not discuss their answers outside your group, unless they give you permission to do so.

TOP FIVE

**Above all,
I think you are:**

1. encouraging
2. shepherding
3. protecting
4. affirming
5. sympathetic

3 RELATIONSHIPS OF TRUST

AFFIRMING YOU Sample Worksheet

What I believe to be true about Pat

FRIEND'S NAME

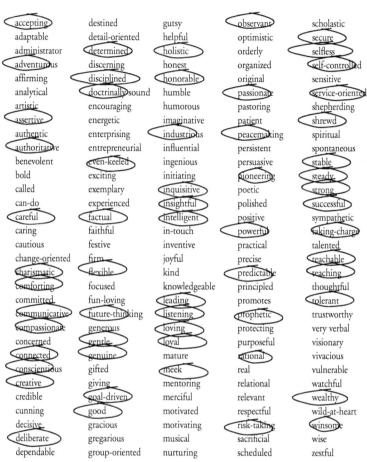

accepting | destined | gutsy | observant | scholastic
adaptable | detail-oriented | helpful | optimistic | secure
administrator | determined | holistic | orderly | selfless
adventurous | discerning | honest | organized | self-controlled
affirming | disciplined | honorable | original | sensitive
analytical | doctrinally sound | humble | passionate | service-oriented
artistic | encouraging | humorous | pastoring | shepherding
assertive | energetic | imaginative | patient | shrewd
authentic | enterprising | industrious | peacemaking | spiritual
authoritative | entrepreneurial | influential | persistent | spontaneous
benevolent | even-keeled | ingenious | persuasive | stable
bold | exciting | initiating | pioneering | steady
called | exemplary | inquisitive | poetic | strong
can-do | experienced | insightful | polished | successful
careful | factual | intelligent | positive | sympathetic
caring | faithful | in-touch | powerful | taking-charge
cautious | festive | inventive | practical | talented
change-oriented | firm | joyful | precise | teachable
charismatic | flexible | kind | predictable | teaching
comforting | focused | knowledgeable | principled | thoughtful
committed | fun-loving | leading | promotes | tolerant
communicative | future-thinking | listening | prophetic | trustworthy
compassionate | generous | loving | protecting | very verbal
concerned | gentle | loyal | purposeful | visionary
connected | genuine | mature | rational | vivacious
conscientious | gifted | meek | real | vulnerable
creative | giving | mentoring | relational | watchful
credible | goal-driven | merciful | relevant | wealthy
cunning | good | motivated | respectful | wild-at-heart
decisive | gracious | motivating | risk-taking | winsome
deliberate | gregarious | musical | sacrificial | wise
dependable | group-oriented | nurturing | scheduled | zestful

NOTES:

I remember last Thursday when the meeting ended, we were all so tired and you revised the agenda for Friday. You have a focused and conscientious quality that makes it clear to everyone where to start on Friday.

LEADERSHIP CATALYST

Please do not duplicate
To order this tool visit
www.leadershipcatalyst.org
Phone: 888.249.0700

WHAT I HEARD ABOUT ME Worksheet

TOP FIVE

What the group believes to be true about me:

Above all, you think I am:

1. _____

2. _____

3. _____

4. _____

5. _____

accepting	destined	gutsy	observant	scholastic
adaptable	detail-oriented	helpful	optimistic	secure
administrator	determined	holistic	orderly	selfless
adventurous	discerning	honest	organized	self-controlled
affirming	disciplined	honorable	original	sensitive
analytical	doctrinally sound	humble	passionate	service-oriented
artistic	encouraging	humorous	pastoring	shepherding
assertive	energetic	imaginative	patient	shrewd
authentic	enterprising	industrious	peacemaking	spiritual
authoritative	entrepreneurial	influential	persistent	spontaneous
benevolent	even-keeled	ingenious	persuasive	stable
bold	exciting	initiating	pioneering	steady
called	exemplary	inquisitive	poetic	strong
can-do	experienced	insightful	polished	successful
careful	factual	intelligent	positive	sympathetic
caring	faithful	in-touch	powerful	taking-charge
cautious	festive	inventive	practical	talented
change-oriented	firm	joyful	precise	teachable
charismatic	flexible	kind	predictable	teaching
comforting	focused	knowledgeable	principled	thoughtful
committed	fun-loving	leading	promotes	tolerant
communicative	future-thinking	listening	prophetic	trustworthy
compassionate	generous	loving	protecting	very verbal
concerned	gentle	loyal	purposeful	visionary
connected	genuine	mature	rational	vivacious
conscientious	gifted	meek	real	vulnerable
creative	giving	mentoring	relational	watchful
credible	goal-driven	merciful	relevant	wealthy
cunning	good	motivated	respectful	wild-at-heart
decisive	gracious	motivating	risk-taking	winsome
deliberate	gregarious	musical	sacrificial	wise
dependable	group-oriented	nurturing	scheduled	zestful

NOTES:

_____

_____

_____

_____

_____

_____

LEADERSHIP CATALYST

Please do not duplicate
To order this tool visit
www.leadershipcatalyst.org
Phone: 888.249.0700

TOP FIVE

**Above all,
I think you are:**

1. *Humble*
2. *listening*
3. *Giving*
4. *Sensitive*
5. *Shepherding*

3 RELATIONSHIPS OF TRUST

AFFIRMING YOU Worksheet

What I believe to be true about *DAVID*

MEMBER'S NAME

accepting	destined	gutsy	observant	scholastic
adaptable	detail-oriented	helpful	optimistic	secure
administrator	determined	holistic	orderly	selfless
adventurous	discerning	honest	organized	self-controlled
affirming	disciplined	honorable	original	sensitive
analytical	doctrinally sound	humble	passionate	service-oriented
artistic	encouraging	humorous	pastoring	shepherding
assertive	energetic	imaginative	patient	shrewd
authentic	enterprising	industrious	peacemaking	spiritual
authoritative	entrepreneurial	influential	persistent	spontaneous
benevolent	even-keeled	ingenious	persuasive	stable
bold	exciting	initiating	pioneering	steady
called	exemplary	inquisitive	poetic	strong
can-do	experienced	insightful	polished	successful
careful	factual	intelligent	positive	sympathetic
caring	faithful	in-touch	powerful	taking-charge
cautious	festive	inventive	practical	talented
change-oriented	firm	joyful	precise	teachable
charismatic	flexible	kind	predictable	teaching
comforting	focused	knowledgeable	principled	thoughtful
committed	fun-loving	leading	promotes	tolerant
communicative	future-thinking	listening	prophetic	trustworthy
compassionate	generous	loving	protecting	very verbal
concerned	gentle	loyal	purposeful	visionary
connected	genuine	mature	rational	vivacious
conscientious	gifted	meek	real	vulnerable
creative	giving	mentoring	relational	watchful
credible	goal-driven	merciful	relevant	wealthy
cunning	good	motivated	respectful	wild-at-heart
decisive	gracious	motivating	risk-taking	winsome
deliberate	gregarious	musical	sacrificial	wise
dependable	group-oriented	nurturing	scheduled	zestful

NOTES:

_____

_____

_____

_____

_____

LEADERSHIP
CATALYST

Please do not duplicate
To order this tool visit
www.leadershipcatalyst.org
Phone: 888.249.0700

PROCESSING THE AFFIRMING EACH OTHER EXPERIENCE

Form one large group and discuss the following question for no more than three minutes: What did you experience? Allow time for everyone who so desires to respond. Stay focused on the processing question and use the guidelines outlined previously to facilitate a healthy discussion.

CLOSING PRAYER

After exploring the processing question together, close in prayer and review the homework for the next session. (see below).

BEFORE THE NEXT SESSION

Read Chapter Five in *The Ascent of a Leader*. Then complete the "Experiencing The Ascent of a Leader on Your Own" section for session four that follows. Pray throughout the week that your discoveries will positively impact all aspects of your everyday life.

RELATIONSHIPS OF TRUST **3**

THE INTEGRATED LADDER

Welcome to Session Four of The Ascent of a Leader *Experience.*

Session Four:

Humility

The first part of each session - Experiencing The Ascent of a Leader on Your Own - includes a number of specific questions based on the related content in *The Ascent of a Leader* book. Take time to read the assigned book chapter, passages from the Bible, and to go through each question on your own. Use the space provided in the Experience Guide to record your thoughts, concerns, questions, and insights.

The second part - Experiencing The Ascent of a Leader Together - is a group experience that expands on the concepts you explored on your own and makes them come alive through creative, focused, and field tested activities. Meet with your group to go through these activities and plan on 30-40 minutes to complete them each session.

Experiencing The Ascent of a Leader on Your Own

PERSONAL PREP
Humility

1 Read Chapter Five in *The Ascent of a Leader* and I Peter 5:5-7. Take time to soak up all the stories and thoughts. This will be the basis for answering the following questions. You may want to review the "Grabbing Hold" questions at the end of the chapter in *The Ascent of a Leader* as well.

2 Get out a pen or pencil and respond to the "Grabbing Hold" questions that follow. Keep in mind this is your personal workbook for examining the truths in *The Ascent of a Leader* and selected passages from the Bible.

GRABBING HOLD
Humility

"Men of genius are admired. Men of wealth are envied. Men of power are feared," Arthur Friedman once said, "but only men of character are trusted." (page 73, *The Ascent of a Leader*)

1. Try to illustrate Friedman's point about our varied responses to different kinds of leaders. For instance, Donald Trump has vast wealth and infamous power to hire or fire—but how many of the people he has influenced would say that they genuinely trust him? Which men or women (from your own experience or the news) come to mind as you consider this statement?

"[People] of genius are admired"   Example:

"[People] of wealth are envied"   Example:

"[People] of power are feared"   Example:

"[People] of character are trusted"   Example:

Do you want to leave a lasting legacy—one that will benefit genera-
tions to come? Do you want to live for a greater purpose—the kind
that will sustain you amid contrary circumstance? Do you long to live
in relationships of trust where you are fully known and know others
more fully? Do you hope for the day when what you do matches who
you are? If so, take the first step up the character ladder." (page 73, *The
Ascent of a Leader*)

2. What does it mean to you to "trust others with who I am"?

The reasons for our trust don't rest solely on the character of those we
choose to follow. Our reasons for trusting can usually be found deep
within our own character as well. (page 65, *The Ascent of a Leader*)

3. The cold hard fact is that trusting is a risky business, especially
when you factor in the very real possibility of disappointment in those
we trust. Recall a specific situation where you found it difficult to trust
someone and one situation where you chose to trust someone. Take
some time to reflect on the core reasons for your choices – especially
any factors of your own character or fears.

"In order to take this step, we must allow the myth of self-sufficiency
to end. In a sense, this means we must let our seed of destiny fall to the
ground and be buried, because this is the only way it can begin to germinate and grow. We must awaken to our need for God and each
other. Whatever hinders our character, whatever fulfillment we lack,
whatever prevents us from reaching our destiny—these things awaken
us to our needs. Needs like these can be met only by placing trust in
God and others. We may be tempted to deny these needs or to try to
meet them through the pursuit of rights or power. But it is our need
for God's care and commitment, our need for others' care and commitment, that motivates us to take the first step in climbing the character
ladder. Without an awareness of our needs, the step is impossible to
take." (page 68, *The Ascent of a Leader*)

4a. Left Foot Up! Imagine yourself stepping up on the first rung of the
Character Ladder—the rung of Humility. Your left foot represents
bursting the myth of self-sufficiency (as happened to Friess when he

HUMILITY 4

watched helplessly while his son almost died). What one experience so far in your life has taught you that self-sufficiency is a myth?

4b. Right Foot Up! Now imagine your right foot stepping up to the Humility rung. It represents the other side of the same coin: the realization that you have needs that you are trusting God and others to meet. What would it look like for you to trust God with one of your deepest needs?

TRUSTING TRUTH
Humility

4c. Both Feet Up! After meditating on the passage below, respond to the questions.

"Living then, as every one of you does, in pure grace, it's important that you not misinterpret yourselves as people who are bringing this goodness to God. No, God brings it all to you. The only accurate way to understand ourselves is by what God is and by what he does for us, not by what we are and what we do for him. In this way we are like the various parts of a human body. Each part gets its meaning from the body as a whole, not the other way around. The body we're talking about is Christ's body of chosen people. Each of us finds our meaning and function as a part of his body. But as a chopped-off finger or cut-off toe we wouldn't amount to much, would we? So since we find ourselves fashioned into all these excellently formed and marvelously functioning parts of Christ's body, let's just go ahead and be what we were made to be, without enviously or pridefully comparing ourselves with each other, or trying to be something we aren't." (Romans 12:3-6, *The Message Bible*)

5. What would it look like for you to trust someone else to meet one of your deepest needs? Be specific about your current need and whom you would trust with that need.

"Trusting God has to do with accepting who God is and accepting who we are in the context of God's plan. It has to do with receiving the protection we need to trust others. Entrusting ourselves to God is the essence of the biblical understanding of humility . . . [U]nless we trust God with our potential, we will be robbed of God's plan for our destiny. When God asks us to let our seed of destiny be buried in the soil of relationship, it is because humility—recognizing that God is God and we are not—is the only catalyst that can enable our character to germinate properly." (page 70, *The Ascent of a Leader*)

6. What do you believe is "catalytic" about humility? In your own words—and in light of God's Word—connect the dots between humility, trust, influence, and destiny.

Experiencing The Ascent of a Leader Together

Before you begin:

1. Get together with your group. If you are a part of a large group (such as a church or school class), your teacher or leader will facilitate the experience. If you're doing this in a small-group setting, anyone can lead the group. If you are the small group leader, review the Leader Guidelines in the Leader's Section on page 118 in the back of this guide.

2. Consider the following guidelines for making the most of your group experience:

▶ When you are directed to form a small group for an activity, *select people you know at least a little*. If you are placed in a pair or trio with people you don't know, take a couple minutes to introduce yourselves. This will give you a good starting place for today's experiential activity.

▶ *Follow the directions carefully*, particularly as they relate to discussion in your small group. These directions have been designed to provide safe boundaries so you can share appropriately with others.

▶ The skills, techniques, and truths you discover during this experience are applicable in many other areas of life. *Practice what you learn outside of this small-group time.*

▶ Above all, *don't be anxious about the experiential activities in this guide*. They aren't scary, "stand up in front of the group and share your life" experiences. Each "Experiencing The Ascent of a Leader Together" activity has been field-tested and is designed to ease you into participation. That's not to say what you learn will be fluffy, surface-level stuff. The experiences can be life-changing. We'll lead you into the deeper stuff. But come prepared to invest yourself in the experience. It will be worth it.

Experiencing The Ascent of a Leader Together

HUMILITY

Welcome

Take a moment to greet one another. If you traditionally enjoy snacks with your group, have at 'em. Use the opening moments as people congregate for a brief time of fellowship.

Small Group Experience

We have selected a few questions from the "Experiencing The Ascent of a Leader on Your Own" section to discuss as a team. Take a few minutes and discuss your responses with your small group. After your discussion, continue your experience with the small group exercise on the following page.

1. What does it mean to you to "trust others with who I am"?

2. The cold hard fact is that trusting is a risky business, especially when you factor in the very real possibility of disappointment in those we trust. Recall a specific situation where you found it difficult to trust someone and one situation where you chose to trust someone. Take some time to reflect on the core reasons for your choices – especially any factors of your own character or fears.

LEADERSHIP
CATALYST

Please do not duplicate
To order this tool visit
www.leadershipcatalyst.org
Phone: 888.249.0700

SUBMITTING TO STRENGTHS

 PERSONAL PREP

In experiencing the Affirming Each Other Experience you processed the first two steps.
1) Declaring another person's strengths
2) Expressing trust in another person's strengths

In this experience you will process steps 3 and 4:
3) Owning the strengths others trust in me
4) Having others submit to the strengths they trust in you

For an Enjoyable Experience

Bring a mindset that says, "I am for the other person's best."

Allow other group members to answer their questions.

Allow other group members to "keep" their answers. Do not correct.

Allow other group members to share their answers. Do not counsel. Listening to others talk about their experience is a wonderful affirmation for them.

Allow other group members to experience safety. Do not discuss their answers outside your group, unless they give you permission to do so.

1 Begin by forming a small group with one or two partners. Groups of three work best. This experience should take approximately 30 minutes.

2 Group Members: Using your Affirming Each Other worksheet Top Five List, choose 3 top strengths you trust in this leader.

_____
_____
_____

3 While each group member is sharing – the member listening should make a list of all trusted strengths declared. For a group of 4 the member may have 3 to 9 strengths. (The leader's own evaluation of his/her strengths not included.)

_____
_____
_____
_____

4 For the Group Member:

1) Do you agree with the group's evaluation of your strengths?
2) What would you change and why?
3) Are you willing to accept (to own) the responsibility of these strengths in influencing your group members? Why or why not?

5 For the Team:

1) Are you willing to accept (to submit to) the influence of this member's strengths in your life? Explain.

2) Discuss how and when you would practically benefit from this member's strengths influencing your life.

NOTES:

_____

_____

_____

_____

_____

_____

_____

_____

_____

_____

_____

_____

LEADERSHIP
CATALYST

Please do not duplicate
To order this tool visit
www.leadershipcatalyst.org
Phone: 888.249.0700

PROCESSING THE SUBMITTING TO STRENGTHS EXPERIENCE

Form one large group and discuss the following question for no more than three minutes: What did you experience? Allow time for everyone who so desires to respond. Stay focused on the processing question and use the guidelines outlined previously to facilitate a healthy discussion.

CLOSING PRAYER

After exploring the processing question together, close in prayer and review the homework for the next session. (see below).

BEFORE THE NEXT SESSION

Read Chapter Six in *The Ascent of a Leader*. Then complete the "Experiencing The Ascent of a Leader on Your Own" section for session five that follows. Pray throughout the week that your discoveries will positively impact all aspects of your everyday life.

4

HUMILITY

NOTES

THE INTEGRATED LADDER

Welcome to Session Five of The Ascent of a Leader *Experience.*

Session Five:

Submission

The first part of each session - Experiencing The Ascent of a Leader on Your Own - includes a number of specific questions based on the related content in *The Ascent of a Leader* book. Take time to read the assigned book chapter, passages from the Bible, and to go through each question on your own. Use the space provided in the Experience Guide to record your thoughts, concerns, questions, and insights.

The second part - Experiencing The Ascent of a Leader Together - is a group experience that expands on the concepts you explored on your own and makes them come alive through creative, focused, and field tested activities. Meet with your group to go through these activities and plan on 30-40 minutes to complete them each session.

Experiencing The Ascent of a Leader on Your Own

PERSONAL PREP
Submission

1 Read Chapter Six in *The Ascent of a Leader* and Ephesians 4:1-3, 5:21. Take time to soak up all the stories and thoughts. This will be the basis for answering the following questions. You may want to review the "Grabbing Hold" questions at the end of the chapter in *The Ascent of a Leader* as well.

2 Get out a pen or pencil and respond to the "Grabbing Hold" questions that follow. Keep in mind this is your personal workbook for examining the truths in *The Ascent of a Leader* and selected passages from the Bible.

GRABBING HOLD
Submission

"Many adults—especially leaders—wander into dark forests of isolation . . . They depend on personal distance for protection . . . [I]nterviews exposed isolation as the primary reason the leaders gave themselves permission to lie. Their isolation was not a spatial separation—people were constantly around these leaders—but a soul separation from others. And it wasn't like the God-appointed isolation God gave Moses in the desert, but rather a state of being lost in Dante's dark wood. Often, the further up leaders are on the capacity ladder or the longer they've occupied the top rung, the worse the problem gets. Isolation factors heavily not only in deception but in many other relational difficulties as well." (pages 75-76, *The Ascent of a Leader*)

1. You've probably heard the saying, "It's lonely at the top." Why do you think that is so often true? Has there been a time when you felt lonely or isolated despite being surrounded by people? As you describe that time, try to identify some effects of your isolation on you—and on others you were influencing.

"Vulnerability does not mean transparency. Transparency is simply disclosing yourself to others at times and in ways that you choose. Although transparency is a good start, in vulnerability you deliberately place yourself under others' influence, submitting yourself to others' strengths. You give others the right to know the pain of your weaknesses and to care for you. You choose to let others know you, to have access to your life, to teach you, and to influence you.

In part, this true vulnerability is what the Bible means when it speaks of submission. Submission is a love word, not a control word. Submission means letting someone love you, teach you, or influence you. In fact, the degree to which we submit to others is the degree to which we will experience their love, regardless of how much love they have for us. Submission goes hand in hand with vulnerability." (page 81, *The Ascent of a Leader*)

2. Let's be sure we are on the same page with our terms. Though related, there are important differences between being transparent, being selectively transparent, and being genuinely vulnerable. Try to illustrate each behavior from your own experience:

I was transparent when . . .

I was selectively transparent when . . .

I was vulnerable when . . .

3. How do you initially react to the word submission? How does thinking of the word submission as a love word and a relationships word change your perspective?

 **TRUSTING TRUTH**
Submission

Read Acts 18:24-28. Describe in your own words Apollo's journey of vulnerability and how this impacted his long-term influence.

> "Vulnerability causes people to know your life is open to them. You are teachable. You will allow the cracks in your life to be not only seen but also filled as you receive their influence. This process expresses your integrity to others, and it helps sustain your integrity . . . Notice that vulnerability triggers two relational effects. First, people gain access to your life as you submit to their influence. Second, you are given access to their lives as they trust you and see that your life is open to them. What do we call this kind of relationship? Authenticity . . . So as we take this second step up the character ladder we must remember, first, that vulnerability means coming under another's influence, submitting to the love they offer; and second, that vulnerability both expresses and sustains integrity, which earns the trust others need in order to submit to our care. Earning the trust of others leads to a natural third result: vulnerability expands influence and productivity." (pages 82-83, *The Ascent of a Leader*)

Few people in popular culture have gained more access to the public's personal lives than Oprah Winfrey. On a recent episode of her television show, Oprah tried to console and encourage women in her audience who had been trying desperately to hide their childhood experiences of abuse. She did so in a risky way by sharing her own similar journey. She told them that she had been sexually assaulted at age 14 and had conceived a child who died two weeks after birth. She had kept this "shameful" event hidden well into her years as a TV celebrity, convinced and terrified that her fans would abandon her if they ever found out. Eventually a disgruntled relative revealed the truth. Oprah was astonished that her fans embraced her instead of rejecting her, and she has learned to be more vulnerable about who she really is and what she struggles with even now. Partly because her audience gained access to her life, she has been given access to theirs.

4. Whose influence do you choose to come into? Why?

Who is choosing to come under your influence? Why?

"The world needs vulnerable leaders—people willing to take the risk of opening their lives to the influence of others. And to find or develop this kind of leader we need to seek out and create environments that encourage such vulnerability. Environments where people know their hearts will not be sacrificed for an agenda—inappropriately called success. Are you ready to live in such an environment? Are you ready to begin building one?" (page 88-89, *The Ascent of a Leader*)

5. Remember the story about Ken? He was so tired that he couldn't think straight. But he risked being vulnerable, even in his "corporate" setting. As a result of Ken stepping up to vulnerability, his teammates " . . . identified Ken's need to be believed. They identified his need for rest. They identified his need to have the details taken care of. (Ken is lousy at planning time off.) They responded with acceptance, affirmation, and with tangible offers of assistance." (page 88, *The Ascent of a Leader*)

How do you respond as you read Ken's story?

Who is providing safety to protect you and your strengths?

"Are you tired of living in the 'dark wood,' feeling isolated and lost though surrounded by others? Do you know two or more people whom you trust implicitly? Are you willing to come under their influence in a much deeper way than you ever thought possible? Are you ready to be vulnerable enough to earn their trust? Becoming vulnerable will both enhance your integrity and express it to others. Does this appeal to you? If so, call those people. Write them. Schedule a time to get together and tell them what's in your heart. Choose vulnerability and then get ready for the next rung." (page 89, *The Ascent of a Leader*)

6. What about you? Set aside time now, or in the next day or two, to talk about these people with God, and listen vulnerably to His response. Summarize below your thoughts of going forward after your time with God.

Experiencing The Ascent of a Leader Together

5
SUBMISSION

Before you begin:

1. Get together with your group. If you are a part of a large group (such as a church or school class), your teacher or leader will facilitate the experience. If you're doing this in a small-group setting, anyone can lead the group. If you are the small group leader, review the Leader Guidelines in the Leader's Section on page 118 in the back of this guide.

2. Consider the following guidelines for making the most of your group experience:

▶ When you are directed to form a small group for an activity, *select people you know at least a little.* If you are placed in a pair or trio with people you don't know, take a couple minutes to introduce yourselves. This will give you a good starting place for today's experiential activity.

▶ *Follow the directions carefully*, particularly as they relate to discussion in your small group. These directions have been designed to provide safe boundaries so you can share appropriately with others.

▶ The skills, techniques, and truths you discover during this experience are applicable in many other areas of life. *Practice what you learn outside of this small-group time.*

▶ Above all, *don't be anxious about the experiential activities in this guide.* They aren't scary, "stand up in front of the group and share your life" experiences. Each "Experiencing The Ascent of a Leader Together" activity has been field-tested and is designed to ease you into participation. That's not to say what you learn will be fluffy, surface-level stuff. The experiences can be life-changing. We'll lead you into the deeper stuff. But come prepared to invest yourself in the experience. It will be worth it.

Experiencing The Ascent of a Leader Together

SUBMISSION

Welcome

Take a moment to greet one another. If you traditionally enjoy snacks with your group, have at 'em. Use the opening moments as people congregate for a brief time of fellowship.

Small Group Experience

We have selected a few questions from the "Experiencing The Ascent of a Leader on Your Own" section to discuss as a team. Take a few minutes and discuss your responses with your small group. After your discussion, continue your experience with the small group exercise on the following page.

1. Let's be sure we are on the same page with our terms. Though related, there are important differences between being transparent, being selectively transparent, and being genuinely vulnerable. Try to illustrate each behavior from your own experience:

I was transparent when . . .

I was selectively transparent when . . .

I was vulnerable when . . .

2. How do you initially react to the word submission? How does thinking of the word submission as a love word and a relationship word change your perspective?

SUBMISSION 5

For an Enjoyable Experience

Bring a mindset that says, "I am for the other person's best."

Allow other group members to answer their questions.

Allow other group members to "keep" their answers. Do not correct.

Allow other group members to share their answers. Do not counsel. Listening to others talk about their experience is a wonderful affirmation for them.

Allow other group members to experience safety. Do not discuss their answers outside your group, unless they give you permission to do so.

LEADERSHIP CATALYST

Please do not duplicate
To order this tool visit
www.leadershipcatalyst.org
Phone: 888.249.0700

ASK ME ANYTHING

PERSONAL PREP

1 Begin by forming a small group with one or two partners. Groups of three work best. This experience should take approximately 30 minutes.

2 On your *Ask Me Anything* worksheet on page 70, write the member's name in the blank provided.

3 Take a few minutes to write five questions you would like this person to answer. Please focus on open-ended, clarifying and affirming types of questions. Avoid questions that force a simple "yes" or "no" answer, as you will miss the opportunity to discover wonderful new insights into this member.

4 Some examples of questions are provided on the sample *Ask Me Anything* worksheet on the next page.

A TIME FOR US

1 Read your five questions from the *Ask Me Anything* worksheet to this member. When you finish, hand your completed worksheet to this member.

2 From your completed worksheet, this member should choose at least two of your questions to answer. This member may choose to answer more, time permitting, but it is entirely the member's choice as to which of your five questions will be answered.

3 While this member is answering at least two questions submitted from each member from the group, take notes of his/her answers.

4 After the questions are answered, discuss as a group what you learned and pray with the member.

ASK ME ANYTHING Sample Worksheet
PART ONE

My five questions for __Pat_____
MEMBER'S NAME

1. What individual whom you know personally do
    you admire most, and why?

2. What is one of the hardest things you have ever
    had to do? Please explain.

3. If you had the time and the money to go any-
    where in the world right now, where would you
    go? Why?

4. What one thing, activity or place most reminds,
    endears and seems to draw you near to God?

5. What do you like best about being on this team?
    Explain.

LEADERSHIP
CATALYST

Please do not duplicate
To order this tool visit
www.leadershipcatalyst.org
Phone: 888.249.0700

ASK ME ANYTHING Worksheet
PART ONE

My five questions for _____
<small>MEMBER'S NAME</small>

1. _____
_____
_____
_____

2. _____
_____
_____
_____

3. _____
_____
_____
_____

4. _____
_____
_____
_____

5. _____
_____
_____
_____

5 SUBMISSION

PROCESSING THE ASK ME ANYTHING EXPERIENCE

Form one large group and discuss the following question for no more than three minutes: What did you experience? Allow time for everyone who so desires to respond. Stay focused on the processing question and use the guidelines outlined previously to facilitate a healthy discussion.

CLOSING PRAYER

After exploring the processing question together, close in prayer and review the homework for the next session (see below).

BEFORE THE NEXT SESSION

Read Chapter Seven in *The Ascent of a Leader*. Then complete the "Experiencing The Ascent of a Leader on Your Own" section for session six that follows. Pray throughout the week that your discoveries will positively impact all aspects of your everyday life.

THE
INTEGRATED
LADDER

Welcome to Session Six of The Ascent of a Leader Experience.

Session Six:

Obedience

The first part of each session - <u>Experiencing The Ascent of a Leader on Your Own</u> - includes a number of specific questions based on the related content in *The Ascent of a Leader* book. Take time to read the assigned book chapter, passages from the Bible, and to go through each question on your own. Use the space provided in the Experience Guide to record your thoughts, concerns, questions, and insights.

The second part - <u>Experiencing The Ascent of a Leader Together</u> - is a group experience that expands on the concepts you explored on your own and makes them come alive through creative, focused, and field tested activities. Meet with your group to go through these activities and plan on 30-40 minutes to complete them each session.

Experiencing The Ascent of a Leader on Your Own

PERSONAL PREP
Obedience

1 Read Chapter Seven in *The Ascent of a Leader* and Colossians 3:12-24. Take time to soak up all the stories and thoughts. This will be the basis for answering the following questions. You may want to review the "Grabbing Hold" questions at the end of the chapter in *The Ascent of a Leader* as well.

2 Get out a pen or pencil and respond to the "Grabbing Hold" questions that follow. Keep in mind this is your personal workbook for examining the truths in *The Ascent of a Leader* and selected passages from the Bible.

GRABBING HOLD
Obedience

"When we ascend the first and second rungs of the character ladder, entrusting our needs to God and others and choosing to open our lives for their review, we soon face the next step—the third rung on the character ladder: align with truth. On this rung we must ask more soul-searching questions. Will I listen to what they say? Do I believe it is true? Will I follow their advice?

This is the true test of character: not just coming under others' influence but acting on the wisdom and truth of their counsel. Aligning with truth distinguishes between those who use transparency to manipulate and those who submit in vulnerability to live lives of integrity." (page 94, *The Ascent of a Leader*)

Let's pause to connect some important dots. We've been comparing the process that leaders go through as they mature to the simple act of climbing a ladder. And we've explored a few key concepts at each step they take. To reinforce your understanding of these concepts, try this exercise:

1. Make an appointment with someone who isn't familiar with *The Ascent of a Leader*. (You get bonus points for doing this with someone under 21!) Ask permission to explain what you are learning about the growth and development of a leader. Using just a blank piece of paper and 15 minutes, draw the ladder and explain the rails and the first three rungs of the ladder as you currently understand them. Here are a few key terms you may want to mention (read "don't have to use") at each step:

After doing this exercise, write out how the experience felt to you and what you learned from it.

THE CHARACTER LADDER

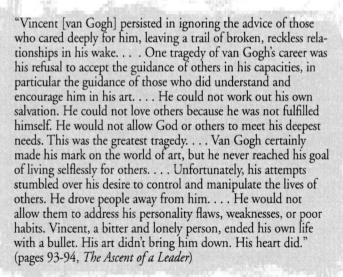

"Vincent [van Gogh] persisted in ignoring the advice of those who cared deeply for him, leaving a trail of broken, reckless relationships in his wake. . . . One tragedy of van Gogh's career was his refusal to accept the guidance of others in his capacities, in particular the guidance of those who did understand and encourage him in his art. . . . He could not work out his own salvation. He could not love others because he was not fulfilled himself. He would not allow God or others to meet his deepest needs. This was the greatest tragedy. . . . Van Gogh certainly made his mark on the world of art, but he never reached his goal of living selflessly for others. . . . Unfortunately, his attempts stumbled over his desire to control and manipulate the lives of others. He drove people away from him. . . . He would not allow them to address his personality flaws, weaknesses, or poor habits. Vincent, a bitter and lonely person, ended his own life with a bullet. His art didn't bring him down. His heart did." (pages 93-94, *The Ascent of a Leader*)

2. Most of us know people whose lives have fallen short of their potential. Maybe we include ourselves among them. Describe someone you know who (in your opinion) ignored advice that

could have helped him/her. What about you? In what ways have you ignored advice that could have helped you? Conversely, describe someone who—when you intentionally shared a need of yours—helped you mature. Looking back from where you are now, what lesson(s) is there for you from those experiences?

3. Eric Bonnehoffer wrote, "Believing is obeying and obeying is believing." What are some of the implications of this relationship of believing (trust) and obedience?

TRUSTING TRUTH
Obedience

4. Jesus met many people who "like most of us, understood the truth intellectually but wanted to define [their] own terms for the expression of love" (page 100, *The Ascent of a Leader*). Read about two of those people in the passages below. What do you think it would have looked like for each of them to take the step to align with and obey the truth that Jesus lovingly offered them?

Luke 10:25-29   Law Expert

Luke 18:18-20   Rich Young Ruler

5. What is the difference between compliance and obedience?

6. Ponder the following statements and then discuss our thoughts using scripture with a key relationship.

Obedience is an expression of our righteousness

God tests our righteousness

Satan tempts our sinfulness

Experiencing The Ascent of a Leader Together

Before you begin:

1. Get together with your group. If you are a part of a large group (such as a church or school class), your teacher or leader will facilitate the experience. If you're doing this in a small-group setting, anyone can lead the group. If you are the small group leader, review the Leader Guidelines in the Leader's Section on page 118 in the back of this guide.

2. Consider the following guidelines for making the most of your group experience:

> When you are directed to form a small group for an activity, *select people you know at least a little.* If you are placed in a pair or trio with people you don't know, take a couple minutes to introduce yourselves. This will give you a good starting place for today's experiential activity.

> *Follow the directions carefully,* particularly as they relate to discussion in your small group. These directions have been designed to provide safe boundaries so you can share appropriately with others.

> The skills, techniques, and truths you discover during this experience are applicable in many other areas of life. *Practice what you learn outside of this small-group time.*

> Above all, *don't be anxious about the experiential activities in this guide.* They aren't scary, "stand up in front of the group and share your life" experiences. Each "Experiencing The Ascent of a Leader Together" activity has been field-tested and is designed to ease you into participation. That's not to say what you learn will be fluffy, surface-level stuff. The experiences can be life-changing. We'll lead you into the deeper stuff. But come prepared to invest yourself in the experience. It will be worth it.

78

Experiencing The Ascent of a Leader Together

OBEDIENCE

Welcome

Take a moment to greet one another. If you traditionally enjoy
snacks with your group, have at 'em. Use the opening moments
as people congregate for a brief time of fellowship.

Small Group Experience

We have selected a few questions from the "Experiencing The
Ascent of a Leader on Your Own" section to discuss as a team.
Take a few minutes and discuss your responses with your small
group. After your discussion, continue your experience with the
small group exercise on the following page.

1. What is the difference between compliance and obedience?

2. Eric Bonnehoffer wrote, "Believing is obeying and obeying is
believing." What are some of the implications of this relationship of believing (trust) and obedience?

For an Enjoyable Experience

Bring a mindset that says, "I am for the other person's best."

Allow other group members to answer their questions.

Allow other group members to "keep" their answers. Do not correct.

Allow other group members to share their answers. Do not counsel. Listening to others talk about their experience is a wonderful affirmation for them.

Allow other group members to experience safety. Do not discuss their answers outside your group, unless they give you permission to do so.

6 OBEDIENCE

LEADERSHIP CATALYST

Please do not duplicate
To order this tool visit
www.leadershipcatalyst.org
Phone: 888.249.0700

ASK ME ANYTHING **PART TWO**

PERSONAL PREP

1 On your *Ask Me Anything* worksheet on the next page, write the member's name in the blank provided.

2 Based on your notes from the member's answers to Ask Me Anything Part One, write five new questions you would like this leader to answer.   Please focus on open-ended, clarifying and affirming types of questions. Avoid questions that force a simple "yes" or "no" answer, as you will miss the opportunity to discover wonderful new insights into this member.

A TIME FOR US

1 Read your five questions from the *Ask Me Anything* worksheet to this leader. When you finish, hand your completed worksheet to this member.

2 From your completed worksheet, this leader should choose at least two of your questions to answer. This leader may choose to answer more, time permitting, but it is entirely your member's choice as to which of your five questions will be answered.

3 While this member is answering at least two questions submitted from the group, take notes of his/her answers for preparing more clarifying questions.

4 While the member is answering the two new questions the member can invite discussion on any point in his/her answers to the questions or clarifying questions

5 After the questions are answered, discuss as a group what you learned and pray with the member.

ASK ME ANYTHING Worksheet
PART TWO

My five new questions for _____
MEMBER'S NAME

1. _____
_____
_____
_____

2. _____
_____
_____
_____

3. _____
_____
_____
_____

4. _____
_____
_____
_____

5. _____
_____
_____
_____

OBEDIENCE 6

LEADERSHIP
CATALYST

Please do not duplicate
To order this tool visit
www.leadershipcatalyst.org
Phone: 888.249.0700

PROCESSING THE ASK ME ANY-THING - PART TWO EXPERIENCE

Form one large group and discuss the following question for no more than three minutes: What did you experience? Allow time for everyone who so desires to respond. Stay focused on the processing question and use the guidelines outlined previously to facilitate a healthy discussion.

CLOSING PRAYER

After exploring the processing question together, close in prayer and review the homework for the next session (see below).

BEFORE THE NEXT SESSION

Read Chapter Eight and Nine in *The Ascent of a Leader*. Then complete the "Experiencing The Ascent of a Leader on Your Own" section for session seven that follows. Pray throughout the week that your discoveries will positively impact all aspects of your everyday life.

6 OBEDIENCE

NOTES

6 OBEDIENCE

THE INTEGRATED LADDER

Welcome to Session Seven of The Ascent of a Leader Experience.

Session Seven:

Suffering

The first part of each session - Experiencing The Ascent of a Leader on Your Own - includes a number of specific questions based on the related content in *The Ascent of a Leader* book. Take time to read the assigned book chapter, passages from the Bible, and to go through each question on your own. Use the space provided in the Experience Guide to record your thoughts, concerns, questions, and insights.

The second part - Experiencing The Ascent of a Leader Together - is a group experience that expands on the concepts you explored on your own and makes them come alive through creative, focused, and field tested activities. Meet with your group to go through these activities and plan on 30-40 minutes to complete them each session.

Experiencing The Ascent of a Leader on Your Own

PERSONAL PREP
Suffering

1 Read Chapters Eight and Nine in *The Ascent of a Leader* and Hebrews 12:1-3. Take time to soak up all the stories and thoughts. This will be the basis for answering the following questions. You may want to review the "Grabbing Hold" questions at the end of the chapter in *The Ascent of a Leader* as well.

2 Get out a pen or pencil and respond to the "Grabbing Hold" questions that follow. Keep in mind this is your personal workbook for examining the truths in *The Ascent of a Leader* and selected passages from the Bible.

GRABBING HOLD
Suffering

"Paying the price means choosing to lead and follow from conviction, rather than reacting to circumstance. It means taking the time to mature, placing a higher value on character than on the short-term benefits of reaching a capacity goal. It means committing to the principles of the long ladder in the context of relationships and environments of grace. As we pay the price, we will learn not to confuse the top of the capacity ladder with the top of the longer ladder. We will accept the consequences of our bad choices, and we will accept the costs of making good choices.

Reaching our destiny requires such testing. Although we may reach certain goals, we will not reach our destiny without the refining and purifying of our hearts. We need the process of the fourth rung in order to mature. This maturity gives us the strength we need to manage our influence well." (pages 135, 130, *The Ascent of a Leader*)

1. Looking Back: In what relationship has your character been tested? How did you deal with that testing?

2. Describe a time one when trusting God with a key relationship meant that you had to suffer (pay a price) for making a choice of integrity. This testing circumstance might have been with colleagues from work, friends from church or your community, or within your marriage or family in which you grew up. In what ways was your objectivity clouded or at risk?

3. Select one or two of these "navigational tips" or "encouraging truths" mentioned in *The Ascent of a Leader* and explain how they might help you reclaim your objectivity in order to help you endure the testing and proving of "paying the price" and suffering.

Navigational Tips:

___ Have a healthy respect for God and for your own limitations in the face of fourth-rung tests.

___ Never put those under your care at great risk for the sake of your own selfish pursuits.

___ Acknowledge that personal testing and risk are unavoidable.

Encouraging Truths:

___ God can be trusted to stand by and support the humble.

___ Many others have gone before you and made it; you are not alone in your ascent.

___ Lean on the lower rungs and find strength in the relationships and environment rails.

How can this tip/truth help you reclaim your objectivity and/or pay the price?

"'Paying the price' implies something that none of us likes to think about. It implies suffering . . . These first three rungs of the character ladder—trust God and others with me, choose vulnerability, and align with truth—correspond very closely with three gracious outcomes—humility, submission, and obedience. Relationships and environments of grace call for leaders who possess these three gracious character traits, because relationships and environments of grace require leaders who possess the ability to love. Let us explain.

To experience the benefits of love, people must receive love. For love to be received, the receiver must trust the giver of love. To be trusted, the giver of love must have integrity. To have integrity, the giver of love must submit to others in vulnerability and align with truth in obedience. At the bottom of all this, givers of love must entrust themselves to God in humility." (pages 113-115, *The Ascent of a Leader*)

 ## TRUSTING TRUTH
Suffering

4. As the authors point out, Jesus is the best example of a servant leader because—from His birth to His death—He paid the price in order to express God's love to humankind and achieve His God-given destiny. Study the three passages below, circling or underlining any clues you notice in Jesus' steps of ascent to "the highest place."

Isaiah 53:10-12 (NLT)

But it was the Lord's good plan to crush him and fill him with grief. Yet when his life is made an offering for sin, he will have a multitude of children, many heirs. He will enjoy a long life, and the Lord's plan will prosper in his hands. [11] When he sees all that is accomplished by his anguish, he will be satisfied. And because of what he has experienced, my righteous servant will make it possible for many to be counted righteous, for he will bear all their sins. [12] I will give him the honors of one who is mighty and great, because he exposed himself to death. He was counted among those who were sinners. He bore the sins of many and interceded for sinners.

Hebrews 5:7-10 (NIV)

During the days of Jesus' life on earth, he offered up prayers and petitions with loud cries and tears to the one who could save him from death, and he was heard because of his reverent submission. [8] Although he was a son, he learned obedience from what he suffered [9] and, once made perfect, he became the source of eternal salvation for all who obey him [10] and was designated by God to be high priest in the order of Melchizedek.

Philippians 2:5-11 (NLT)

Your attitude should be the same that Christ Jesus had. [6] Though he was God, he did not demand and cling to his rights as God. [7] He made himself nothing; he took the humble position of a slave and appeared in human form. [8] And in human form he obediently humbled himself even further by dying a criminal's death on a cross. [9] Because of this, God raised him up to the heights of heaven and gave him a name that is above every other name, [10] so that at the name of Jesus every knee will bow, in heaven and on earth and under the earth, [11] and every tongue will confess that Jesus Christ is Lord, to the glory of God the Father.

Record your observations about Jesus' ascent beside the appropriate steps on this ladder. (And by the way, now you know the primary passages of Scripture that inspired the ladder illustration!)

THE CHARACTER LADDER

SUFFERING 7

THE CHARACTER LADDER

5. With whom do you stand today in guarding and protecting you from falling off Rung 4? Who protects you in your destiny?

6. Looking Ahead: Are you ready to count the cost of the fourth rung in order to prepare for your destiny? Explain.

If not for yourself, would you do it for the benefit of others? Explain.

For the honor of God? Explain.

For the sake of love? Explain.

 TRUSTING TRUTH

7. Read I Peter 2:20-21, 4:12-19

What is the suffering that is unique to the Christian? How does it differ from the suffering which is common to man?

NOTES

Experiencing The Ascent of a Leader Together

Before you begin:

1. Get together with your group. If you are a part of a large group (such as a church or school class), your teacher or leader will facilitate the experience. If you're doing this in a small-group setting, anyone can lead the group. If you are the small group leader, review the Leader Guidelines in the Leader's Section on page 118 in the back of this guide.

2. Consider the following guidelines for making the most of your group experience:

> ▶ When you are directed to form a small group for an activity, *select people you know at least a little*. If you are placed in a pair or trio with people you don't know, take a couple minutes to introduce yourselves. This will give you a good starting place for today's experiential activity.

> ▶ *Follow the directions carefully*, particularly as they relate to discussion in your small group. These directions have been designed to provide safe boundaries so you can share appropriately with others.

> ▶ The skills, techniques, and truths you discover during this experience are applicable in many other areas of life. *Practice what you learn outside of this small-group time.*

> ▶ Above all, *don't be anxious about the experiential activities in this guide*. They aren't scary, "stand up in front of the group and share your life" experiences. Each "Experiencing The Ascent of a Leader Together" activity has been field-tested and is designed to ease you into participation. That's not to say what you learn will be fluffy, surface-level stuff. The experiences can be life-changing. We'll lead you into the deeper stuff. But come prepared to invest yourself in the experience. It will be worth it.

7

SUFFERING

Experiencing The Ascent of a Leader Together

SUFFERING

Welcome

Take a moment to greet one another. If you traditionally enjoy snacks with your group, have at 'em. Use the opening moments as people congregate for a brief time of fellowship.

Small Group Experience

We have selected a few questions from the "Experiencing The Ascent of a Leader on Your Own" section to discuss as a team. Take a few minutes and discuss your responses with your small group. After your discussion, continue your experience with the small group exercise on the following page.

1. Describe a time one when trusting God with a key relationship meant that you had to suffer (pay a price) for making a choice of integrity. This testing circumstance might have been with colleagues from work, friends from church or your community, or within your marriage or family in which you grew up. In what ways was your objectivity clouded or at risk?

2. With whom do you stand today in guarding and protecting you from falling off Rung 4? Who protects you in your destiny?

For an Enjoyable Experience

Bring a mindset that says, "I am for the other person's best."

Allow other group members to answer their questions.

Allow other group members to "keep" their answers. Do not correct.

Allow other group members to share their answers. Do not counsel. Listening to others talk about their experience is a wonderful affirmation for them.

Allow other group members to experience safety. Do not discuss their answers outside your group, unless they give you permission to do so.

PAYING THE PRICE

PERSONAL PREP

1 On the *Paying the Price* worksheet on page 96, in the first column entitled "Circumstance," identify one personal example of a choice you had to make where you had to "Pay the Price" for making a right decision. A sample of a completed *Paying the Price* worksheet is provided on the next page to help you.

2 In the second column, entitled "Price I had to consider," describe your feelings when you realized that you had to make the right decision.

3 In the third column, entitled "What I did," describe your attitude, actions and expectations. What did you do in response to those who disagreed with you and your actions?

A TIME FOR US

1 Share your experiences from the *Paying the Price* worksheet with each other.

2 As a group, listen carefully to the member as he/she shares, noting disappointments, feelings expressed and reactions.

3 After the member is finished, discuss the following questions, noting your answers on the *Paying the Price Resolution* worksheet on page 97:
• If you had made a different choice, what would have happened?
• How did you feel after your choice?

7
SUFFERING

LEADERSHIP
CATALYST

Please do not duplicate
To order this tool visit
www.leadershipcatalyst.org
Phone: 888.249.0700

PAYING THE PRICE Sample Worksheet

CIRCUMSTANCE	PRICE I HAD TO CONSIDER	WHAT I DID
At 3 PM on Wednesday our chairman called to tell me without prior discussion that I needed to let 3 staff go. On Friday, 1 of the staff was not to be fired. The chairman was instrumental in recently hiring this staff member.	Anger. Demeaned. Struggled with issues of compliance. Worried about my reaction even if my own staff position was safe.	I withdrew to pull myself together I instantly knew this was the issue that would cause me to face the issues of my leadership, submission, my convictions. I called the chairman for a meeting of all the leadership team to address and process issues of fairness. I was ultimately dismissed for my decision about fairness. None of the relationships are resolved.

LEADERSHIP CATALYST

Please do not duplicate
To order this tool visit
www.leadershipcatalyst.org
Phone: 888.249.0700

PAYING THE PRICE Worksheet

**LEADERSHIP
CATALYST**

Please do not duplicate
To order this tool visit
www.leadershipcatalyst.org
Phone: 888.249.0700

CIRCUMSTANCE	PRICE I HAD TO CONSIDER	WHAT I DID

7

SUFFERING

PAYING THE PRICE RESOLUTION
Worksheet

If you had made a different choice, what would have happened?

_____

_____

_____

_____

_____

_____

_____

_____

_____

How did you feel after your choice?

_____

_____

_____

_____

_____

_____

_____

_____

_____

_____

PROCESSING THE PAYING THE PRICE EXPERIENCE

Form one large group and discuss the following question for no more than three minutes: What did you experience? Allow time for everyone who so desires to respond. Stay focused on the processing question and use the guidelines outlined previously to facilitate a healthy discussion.

CLOSING PRAYER

After exploring the processing question together, close in prayer and review the homework for next week's session (see below).

BEFORE THE NEXT SESSION

Read Chapters Ten, Eleven and Twelve in *The Ascent of a Leader*. Then complete the "Experiencing The Ascent of a Leader on Your Own" section for session eight that follows. Pray throughout the week that your discoveries will positively impact all aspects of your everyday life.

7 SUFFERING

NOTES

**THE
INTEGRATED
LADDER**

Welcome to Week Eight of The Ascent of a Leader *Experience.*

Session Eight:

Destiny

The first part of each week - <u>Experiencing The Ascent of a Leader on Your Own</u> - includes a number of specific questions based on the related content in *The Ascent of a Leader* book. Take time to read the assigned book chapter, passages from the Bible, and to go through each question on your own. Use the space provided in the Experience Guide to record your thoughts, concerns, questions, and insights.

The second part - <u>Experiencing The Ascent of a Leader Together</u> - is a group experience that expands on the concepts you explored on your own and makes them come alive through creative, focused, and field tested activities. Meet with your group to go through these activities and plan on 30-40 minutes to complete them each week.

DESTINY 8

Experiencing The Ascent of a Leader on Your Own

PERSONAL PREP
Destiny

1 Read Chapters Ten, Eleven and Twelve in *The Ascent of a Leader,* Philippians 2:5-11, and I Peter 5:5-6. Take time to soak up all the stories and thoughts. This will be the basis for answering the following questions. You may want to review the "Grabbing Hold" questions at the end of the chapter in *The Ascent of a Leader* as well.

2 Get out a pen or pencil and respond to the "Grabbing Hold" questions that follow. Keep in mind this is your personal workbook for examining the truths in *The Ascent of a Leader* and selected passages from the Bible.

GRABBING HOLD
Destiny

"When we replace the shaky rails of the shorter ladder with the strong rails of relationships and environments of grace, we can attach them to the rails of the character ladder in a sturdy fashion. Thus, as illustrated in Figure 10.2, the character ladder can function like an extension, leveraging our capacities far beyond what we could have accomplished without character. Ordinary people in ordinary relationships can do extraordinary things with such an integrated ladder." (page 143, *The Ascent of a Leader*)

1. Open to the illustration on page 144 in your book. In chapters 9 and 10 you read about President Jimmy Carter, Mother Teresa, and General George Marshall—all people who rose from

relative obscurity to world prominence later in life. Their secret to destiny?—each of them integrated the two ladders by finding "relationships and environments of grace that would honor their capacities while nurturing their character." What about in your experience? Who do you know that is influencing people today because he/she integrated the two ladders well? Explain.

"When we examine the natural talents of great influencers [like those mentioned above] we often find little that distinguishes them from others. But when we look at their character, we find the essential ingredients of their greatness. They trusted God and others. They chose vulnerability. They aligned with truth and paid the price for their decisions. God then elevated these prepared people to positions of honor and influence beyond their potential apart from the character ladder." (page 146, *The Ascent of a Leader*)

 **TRUSTING TRUTH**
Destiny

2. At the top of the integrated ladder you will find what you would never find climbing just the capacity ladder: destiny. Destiny is your God-given position of honor and influence beyond your own potential on your own. Study these passages describing how a leader ascends / is exalted / is lifted up. Then summarize what part God plays—and what part you play—in reaching your destiny.

I Samuel 2:6-10

Philippians 2:5-11

DESTINY 8

Luke 18:9-14

I Peter 5:5-6

II Samuel 12:7-9

Summary:

"Discovering destiny is far from passive. In fact, it may be the most active rung of all. The fifth rung presents us with at least seven significant challenges. If we don't welcome these challenges, our refusal will keep us from discovering our destiny. Those who have made it to the fifth rung risk slipping off if they forget to actively greet these challenges. They may finish their lives poorly, losing the influence they have gained . . . You cannot plan your destiny, but you can prepare for it." (pages 147, 164, *The Ascent of a Leader*)

3. Most of us have not yet reached the fifth rung in our personal and leadership journeys. Discovering, much less achieving, our destinies still lie ahead of us. But wherever we are now, we can be preparing for the fifth rung by embracing some of its challenges.

Review the seven significant challenges of the fifth rung on the next page. Choose several of them, and describe what it would look like in very practical terms if you were to step up to these challenges in your context over the next months.

8

DESTINY

Confronting my complacency to keep pursuing goals	
Seeking opportunities to serve others from my heart	
Continuing to change, grow, and learn, while mentoring & teaching others	
Trusting my influence to God (not comparing with others)	
Sharing the benefits of my influence with others (not just benefiting from them)	
Staying fluid by balancing my time, relationship, and priorities	
Inviting others to help me resolve my character issues and weaknesses	

In the next few months, if I really wanted to get serious about:

I would:

Now go back and select one challenge. Elevate it from the realm of "if," then using what you have learned in climbing the integrated ladder, describe with a key relationship how in trusting God you will start implementing this challenge.

4. What are the challenges in living for the benefit of those you influence?

"As we each participate in the making of the work of art called our lives, we must learn to master the tools God has given us. A painter has brushes, oils, and canvas. To develop character, we have principles, relationships, and environments. But reading about the tools, as you have in this book, cannot make you a master any more than reading about painting will make you a great painter. To become a painter, you must start painting. To develop character, you must begin climbing the character ladder. But how? Begin with community. Community happens one relationship at a time; therefore it is never beyond your grasp." (page 175, *The Ascent of a Leader*)

5. When you consider the people in your work, social circle, church, and family contexts, whom are you willing to trust with you? Who are the:

> People with whom you can explore inner needs and strengths alongside issues of capacity?

> Allies who are willing to stand with you?

> Ordinary people who are willing to tell you the truth and who will also receive truth from you?

> Friends who with you are discovering God's destiny for your life?

This is the community you need to develop your character, to discover your destiny.

Describe how you will implement with these people the truths you are experiencing in the process of using this guide.

6a. Consider these statements:

The mature own the influence of their person in:

▶ Delighting in the success of others.

8 DESTINY

▶ Searching for ways to care for and improve the circumstance of others.

▶ Benefiting with their team and community.

▶ Suffering for and in the consequences of paying the price for decisions of integrity.

6b. Spend at least ten minutes in undisturbed listening prayer then answer these questions:

When you pause to hear the cries of those around you, what do you hear?

When you pause to hear the cry within your own heart, what do you hear?

Experiencing The Ascent of a Leader Together

Before you begin:

1. Get together with your group. If you are a part of a large group (such as a church or school class), your teacher or leader will facilitate the experience. If you're doing this in a small-group setting, anyone can lead the group. If you are the small group leader, review the Leader Guidelines in the Leader's Section on page 118 in the back of this guide.

2. Consider the following guidelines for making the most of your group experience:

▶ When you are directed to form a small group for an activity, *select people you know at least a little.* If you are placed in a pair or trio with people you don't know, take a couple minutes to introduce yourselves. This will give you a good starting place for today's experiential activity.

▶ *Follow the directions carefully*, particularly as they relate to discussion in your small group. These directions have been designed to provide safe boundaries so you can share appropriately with others.

▶ The skills, techniques, and truths you discover during this experience are applicable in many other areas of life. *Practice what you learn outside of this small-group time.*

▶ Above all, *don't be anxious about the experiential activities in this guide.* They aren't scary, "stand up in front of the group and share your life" experiences. Each "Experiencing The Ascent of a Leader Together" activity has been field-tested and is designed to ease you into participation. That's not to say what you learn will be fluffy, surface-level stuff. The experiences can be life-changing. We'll lead you into the deeper stuff. But come prepared to invest yourself in the experience. It will be worth it.

8

DESTINY

Experiencing The Ascent of a Leader Together

DESTINY

Welcome

Take a moment to greet one another. If you traditionally enjoy snacks with your group, have at 'em. Use the opening moments as people congregate for a brief time of fellowship.

Small Group Experience

We have selected a few questions from the "Experiencing The Ascent of a Leader on Your Own" section to discuss as a team. Take a few minutes and discuss your responses with your small group. After your discussion, continue your experience with the small group exercise on the following page.

1. When you consider the people in your work, social circle, church, and family contexts, whom are you willing to trust with you?

Who are the: People with whom you can explore inner needs and strengths alongside issues of capacity?

Allies who are willing to stand with you?

Ordinary people who are willing to tell you the truth and who will also receive truth from you?

Friends who with you are discovering God's destiny for your life?

This is the community you need to develop your character, to discover your destiny. Describe how you will implement with these people the truths you are experiencing in the process of using this guide.

2. What are the challenges in living for the benefit of those you influence?

For an Enjoyable Experience

Bring a mindset that says, "I am for the other person's best."

Allow other group members to answer their questions.

Allow other group members to "keep" their answers. Do not correct.

Allow other group members to share their answers. Do not counsel. Listening to others talk about their experience is a wonderful affirmation for them.

Allow other group members to experience safety. Do not discuss their answers outside your group, unless they give you permission to do so.

"There is no greater failure than to come to that moment for which one was designed...and not be prepared."

LEADERSHIP
CATALYST

Please do not duplicate
To order this tool visit
www.leadershipcatalyst.org
Phone: 888.249.0700

8 DESTINY

OWNING YOUR INFLUENCE

PERSONAL PREP

1 Each member of the group will personally reflect on their destiny and answer the two questions below:

Question #1 In what opportunity (relationship, event, role) do you think God may be wanting to exalt you--to deepen or expand your influence?

Note: There will be many times in our lives when God lifts us up to the fifth rung to fulfill an assignment for Him in the kingdom; and it will always involve others. While we may be aware of an overarching destiny in our lives, there are many "destiny events." So, you don't need to search for your "big destiny" to answer this question.

Question #2 What item from the two rails or five rungs (The Catalyst Trust Model™) do you believe could better prepare you to receive God's fifth rung exaltation in your life?

Note: If you cannot think of a specific area, pick a date by which you will meet with someone that knows you well to discuss these questions.

PROCESSING THE OWNING YOUR INFLUENCE EXPERIENCE

Form one large group and discuss the following question for no more than three minutes: What did you experience? Allow time for everyone who so desires to respond. Stay focused on the processing question and use the guidelines outlined previously to facilitate a healthy discussion.

CLOSING PRAYER

After exploring the processing question together, close in prayer.

DESTINY 8

**THE
INTEGRATED
LADDER**

LEADER'S GUIDE

Welcome

You are about to embark on an amazing journey. A journey that could change your life—and the lives of those entrusted to you as the leader of The Ascent of a Leader Experience. The Ascent of a Leader Experience is more than a collection of interactive activities and personal reflection—it's a carefully crafted eight-session encounter that can free people to discover the dreams and destiny God has prepared for them.

Whether you're a pastor, a church school teacher, a team manager, or a small-group leader, the information in this guide will help you facilitate a successful Ascent of a Leader Experience. If you haven't already read *The Ascent of a Leader*, start there. Get to know the life-changing message of this book. Then spend time in prayer, asking God to work in the hearts of those who will go through this experience. Finally, when you're ready to lead, read on and discover the keys to making your Ascent Experience a success.

How to Lead The Ascent of a Leader Experience

Understanding the Experience

The Ascent of a Leader Experience is an eight-session small group experience. Because much of the experience is accomplished in small groups (of two to four people), you can facilitate this in just about any setting. It works as an eight-session Sunday school curriculum for a large class as easily as it does for a home group.

Each participant in the experience will need a copy of the book *The Ascent of a Leader* and a copy of *The Ascent of a Leader Experience Guide. The Ascent of a Leader Experience Guide* is a session-by-session workbook that includes self-study material (in a section called "Experiencing The Ascent On Your Own") and instructions for the small-group experiences you'll be leading (in a section called "Experiencing The Ascent of a Leader Together.")

Your Role as Leader

Your role for The Ascent of a Leader Experience is that of a facilitator. If you're in charge of a whole-church experience or any other large-group experience, you'll want to plan the eight-session event well in advance so you have time to advertise the experience as well as collect necessary supplies (books and experience guides).

No matter what the size of your group, you'll be responsible to arrange for the availability of snacks or coffee. During each specific session, you will simply lead participants through the "Experiencing The Ascent of a Leader Together" section of the Experience Guide. (Clear instructions are given for each session.) It's that easy!

It's important to note that you are a facilitator and not a teacher for this experience. Follow the instructions closely and fight the temptation to expand on the material provided. This is a place for experiential learning, not lecture. Participants will make their greatest personal discoveries as they go through the various exercises and process them together.

Refer to the Tips for Leading a Small Group section that follows for more help as you facilitate The Ascent of a Leader Experience.

Leading the "Experiencing The Ascent of a Leader Together" Sessions
As the group leader, you're responsible to keep things moving so the "Experiencing The Ascent of a Leader Together" sessions don't run too long. We've designed these to fit within a typical small group meeting time or Sunday school class (45 to 50 minutes). In order to stay on schedule, follow the instructions closely and make sure your small groups are no larger than three people (or as otherwise directed in *The Ascent of a Leader Experience Guide*).

Use the following "snapshot" of the session elements to help you as you plan your meeting time. Keep in mind the listed times are guidelines, not hard-and-fast rules. But also keep in mind that it's important to show group members you value their time—don't allow sessions to go significantly longer than advertised.

SESSIONS ONE THROUGH SEVEN:
Welcome	(2-3 minutes)
Introduce the Experience	(1 minute)
Complete The Ascent of a Leader Experience	(25-30 minutes)
Process the The Ascent of a Leader Experience	(3-5 minutes)
Pray and plan for the coming week	(2-3 minutes)

SESSION EIGHT:
Welcome	(2-3 minutes)
Introduce the Experience	(1 minute)
Complete the The Ascent of a Leader Experience	(15-20 minutes)
Process the The Ascent of a Leader Experience	(10 minutes)
Pray and close the session	(2-3 minutes)

Tips for Leading a Small Group

Prepare ahead of time.

Make sure everyone has the necessary materials before the session. Each person should have a copy of *The Ascent of a Leader* and a copy of the *The Ascent of a Leader Experience Guide*.

Follow the directions carefully.

Each experience has been designed to lead participants toward significant personal discovery. Following rabbit trails can detract from this goal. Stay on task and follow the instructions given. If group members lose the point or try to forge new paths that move outside of the experience, kindly redirect them and make plans to talk about those things after the session is over.

Set clear expectations for the group.

Ask group members to make a commitment to the entire eight-session experience. Significant personal growth occurs when group members build relationships and their understanding of the material session by session. But also be realistic. Sometimes people can't make it to a session. When this happens, be sure to let group members know that they're welcome to return the following session.

Agree together that everyone's story is important. Small-group discussion times are to be shared by all members, not hijacked by a single group member.

Help keep small-group members on task by letting them know when it's time for the next person to share during timed small-group activities.

Be consistent.

After you choose your time and place for the sessions, stick to these. Changing locations or times may discourage participants or cause them to stop coming. Consistency removes stress that could otherwise frustrate discussion and subsequent personal growth.

Respect everyone's time.

Start on time. We encourage beginning a session with a few minutes for snacks and casual conversation, but don't let that time steal from the The Ascent of a Leader Experience. Also, be sure to end on time (or ask permission to extend the time if you know you're going to run late during a given session). People will have no qualms about making a commitment to your group if you stick to your timetable and communicate any variances from that plan.

Embrace appropriate silence.

In a classroom setting, silence may seem like the "kiss of death" during a discussion time. It may make you feel uncomfortable. Be patient when the group is quiet. Sometimes participants need time to quietly reflect and think before sharing from their heart. This kind of silence is a good thing. Allow conversations, discussions, and small-group activities to develop naturally.

Be an encourager.

Some participants may be anxious about the experiential activities in this guide. Let them know that these aren't scary, "stand up in front of the group and share your life" experiences. Reassure group members that each activity was developed with their safety and protection in mind.

Trust the Holy Spirit.

While there may be times when personal growth is visibly evident in group members, you will probably experience more times than not when you question if group members are really learning or growing. Hang in there through the eight sessions and stick to the program. Don't attempt to force learning. Instead, use your energy to pray and ask the Holy Spirit to do the work of changing lives. Just because you don't see evidence of change doesn't mean the Holy Spirit isn't initiating it.

Pray.

Pray before you begin each session. Pray to open and close each session. Pray intensely and often that God would impact the lives of the participants (that means you, too) throughout this experience.

Leader Guidelines

If you are the designated leader for The Ascent of a Leader Experience, please follow these guidelines to ensure a positive experience for all participants.

1. Make sure everyone has the necessary materials before the session. Each person should have a copy of the book *The Ascent of a Leader* and a copy of *The Ascent of a Leader Experience Guide*.

2. Review the group questions for each session. Each session has two questions from the "Experiencing The Ascent of a Leader on Your Own" section that your group will discuss.

3. Review the Experience for each session. Each Experience leads your small group in experiencing the truth presented in each session. It is the critical part of each session.

4. You are the facilitator for this, not a teacher. Follow the instructions closely and fight any temptation to expand on the material provided. This is a place for experiential learning, *not* lecture.

5. Don't worry if some questions are left unanswered. Unanswered questions are part of the discovery process.

6. Close the session with prayer, and remind your group of their homework assignments for the coming session.

COACH TOOLS

The tools on the following pages are provided for trained Leadership Catalyst Coaches. It contains the outlines and scripts for each of the eight coach delivered sessions.

For more information about Leadership Catalyst services and resources, please visit our website at leadershipcatalyst.org.

CHARACTER AND CAPACITY

Are you the kind of person who others want to follow or *have* to follow?

Roles are essential in organizations, but the ultimate influence of your life will come more from

_____ than even

_____.

Leading from this influence requires a special quality that leading from position or power does not: Trust.

Influence is based on trust and this trust is anchored in two components: Character and Capacity.

Surveys from business, education, government and military indicate that the quality with the greatest gap between what followers most want in their leaders and what they actually receive is trust.

We call this The Trust Gap.

Most people discover their lives are like the Capacity Ladder.

At the top of the Capacity Ladder are stressors and strains one never experienced at the bottom:

- ▶ Pressure of _____
- ▶ Temptation of _____
- ▶ Demands of _____
- ▶ Drain of _____
- ▶ Isolation of _____

THE CAPACITY LADDER

These capacity rungs are important to personal development, but when character is assumed it leads to _____ of the ladders (of life).

A disintegrated life results in:
- ▶ Relational Struggles
- ▶ Emotional Immaturity
- ▶ Lost Opportunities
- ▶ Failure and Falling

Nothing hides disintegration like success for a season.

The critical question for any person is "How do I _____ my life? How do I put these two ladders together?"

THE CHARACTER LADDER

CHARACTER AND CAPACITY

THE CAPACITY LADDER

Are you the kind of person that people want to follow or have to follow? What if you were falsely accused by someone in or outside your organization? Would your people stand by you? You may know success in your field, but to what extent will people follow you? Would your people die for you? If you were diagnosed with a debilitating illness, would they openly express sadness, but privately find relief in the possible transition of the role you occupy?

Living and leading in the high-trust culture is primarily about who we are—about our influence—not about our role or our financial success. Roles are important in organizations, but in your life your ultimate influence will come more from who you are than from what you do—more from your relationships than from the position you occupy or titles you hold.

In the high-trust culture, any person of influence will lead others to some degree, regardless of title or position. Leading from who you are requires a special power that leading from role or position do not. It requires the power of trust.

You don't need trust to lead from role. "Why can't I have the car keys?" "Because I said so, and I'm your dad." "Why should I tell them you're out of the office, when you're really in?" "Because, that's the way we do it around here...I'm the boss."

People base their trust on two things: who people are and what people do. In other words, people trust others based on an evaluation of character and capacity. The vast majority of leaders train or develop the part most easily seen—their capacity—and neglect what is unseen beneath the surface—their character. But both being and doing are important for leading from influence.

Surveys from business, education, and government demonstrate that the greatest gap between what followers most want in their leaders and what leaders actually provide is trust. We call this "The Trust Gap." People everywhere long to close The Trust Gap in their workplaces, their churches, their marriages, their families and their friendships.

THE CHARACTER LADDER

While it may be less evident or obvious in a person's development, character development should not be left to chance. Character is about who we are. It is about "being" instead of "doing."

Yet, most people discover their lives and leadership are like the Capacity Ladder. You could call it the career ladder or the competency ladder because it's all about getting to the top of our game, to the pinnacle of what we think we're supposed to do in life. It can be applied to having a wonderful family, leading a successful business, creating works of art, pastoring a healthy church, or mastering your golf game.

Typically, the Capacity Ladder begins with a person's natural leadership—a winsome personality, a dynamic influence, an ability to persuade or to craft a compelling vision (rung one). More influence is granted as one adds the second rung of developing talents and gifts, often trained in colleges and grad schools and honed in the leader's first companies, organizations or churches.

Successfully scaling the first two rungs attracts the attention of executives, administrators, professors and thousands of people who choose their leaders. This catapults the person to the third rung, where decision-makers and followers award a title, position or office, leading naturally to the fourth rung—achieving potential.

The climb itself is challenging and unpredictable, often stable at the bottom and shaky at the top, like a real ladder. From the bottom, life at the top looks appealing, even alluring, and many leaders attack the ladder with gusto, confident they possess what it takes to conquer the rungs—and you know what? They do.

When a person reaches positions of authority on the Capacity Ladder, unforeseen instability begins to surface. Things one could not have imagined at the bottom come into clear view. Issues like the pressure of success, the temptation of privilege, the demands of followers, the drain of critics, and the isolation of leadership leave white-knuckle impressions on the rungs.

Is there anything wrong with the rungs on the Capacity Ladder? Not a thing. They represent the training of our God-given capacities, particularly our gifts and talents. Therefore, these capacity rungs are important for personal development, but when character is assumed it leads to disintegration of the ladders (of life).

We need the Character Ladder in our lives. As you view the natural sequence of the five rungs of the Character Ladder, a famous scripture may have come to your mind. The Character Ladder was perfectly modeled by Jesus, and it is summarized in Philippians 2. Many other scriptures also support the construction of the Character Ladder. We will invest the remaining modules of The Ascent Experience in climbing the rungs of this Character Ladder.

Neglecting the climb up the Character Ladder or just assuming the rungs have been ascended leads to significant life problems: Life issues like relational struggles, dysfunction, disappointment, failure and even falling off the upper rungs of the Capacity Ladder.

And, here's a crucial concept: Nothing hides disintegration like success . . . for a season.

After a season or two at the top of the Capacity Ladder, many leaders begin to reflect on how they got to the top of this short career ladder. They remember what they didn't deal with on the way up, and now, in their position of influence, you can rest assured they will not talk to others about these things. Why? We moved them to a place where what they're going to lose is so great that they can never share what's true about themselves. A system that rewards brilliance and charisma at the expense of the leader's disclosure will create leaders who hide their issues in an attempt to reach their goals. This is called isolation. This is called pressure. If you're at the bottom and you fall, it doesn't hurt! But, if you're at the top and you fall it could be life-threatening or career-ending. Ironically and tragically, many leaders do not show evidence of cracking until they are at the apex of their influence, when the weight from the fruit of their leadership is greatest.

Feeling this pressure, many look for a way to shore up their situation. Some manage to hang on at the top, in an isolated, busy, unfulfilled life. Many others who cannot hang on at the top come crashing down. When this person hits bottom, there are few around to help. Fewer still know how to help. Many will simply tell the leader, "You're an embarrassment. Tell you what, why don't you just pick up your little Capacity Ladder and take it somewhere else." That's why you find so many leaders in business or the church who have left too many places and too many friendships by their 40th or 50th birthday.

Character is designed to protect and leverage our capacities. The dysfunction in many leaders today is rooted in a common reality: their skills and capacities have been intentionally trained while their character has been merely presumed. This leaves both their character undeveloped and their capacities at risk.

Do you know leaders who have all the Capacity Ladder rungs in place, including the success from their influence, and yet you sense something wrong? Talent, gift, accomplishment, material assets and performance shine in these people, but immaturity in character, illustrated through relational issues, tarnishes their influence. The irony: A leader firmly lodged at the top of the Capacity Ladder may not have begun to climb the Character Ladder. This gap creates the phenomenon we call "big leaders on short ladders."

The ultimate question for any person or leader is, "How do I integrate my life? How do I put these two ladders together?" Not "Should I integrate?", but "How do I integrate my life?" Ultimately, trust can integrate these two ladders…creating a soaring Ladder of Influence, where people discover destinies beyond their imaginations.

NOTES

_____

_____

_____

_____

_____

_____

_____

_____

_____

_____

_____

_____

_____

_____

_____

_____

_____

ENVIRONMENTS OF GRACE

The rails integrate the ladders.

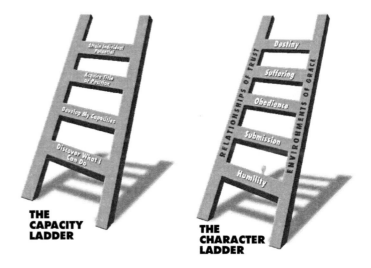

THE CAPACITY LADDER

THE CHARACTER LADDER

The rails are the missing components in many spiritual development programs today.

The rails combine to create a community of grace, where

_____ is developed.

_____ is built.

_____ is told.

Life is _____ (truefaced).

The Environment of Grace changes our life focus:

Working on my Sin Issues ⟶

Trusting who God says I am ⟶

How I view me may be the most revealing commentary of my theology.

The Qualities of an Environment of Grace.

Grace changes how we treat each other and our sin issues.

A _____ sinner or a

_____ who sins.

THE INTEGRATED LADDER

ENVIRONMENTS OF GRACE

There are seven components in this character ladder. Five rungs, humility, submission, obedience, suffering, exaltation, and then two incredible rails: Relationships of Trust and Environments of Grace.

The first thing we notice is that the rails integrate the ladders, creating one soaring ladder of influence. These rails are crucial to integrating my life—my being with my doing

Both of these rails are absolutely critical to the formation of our character, and yet the rails are the missing components in most spiritual and character development programs today. Many times, the models for spiritual formation are isolation models, in contrast to relational models.

The rails create a sturdy and safe way for people and leaders to climb the capacity and character rungs. There's a lot more than meets the eye in the stuff of these rails. They are filled with many qualities, many of which we'll discover as we proceed through The Ascent of a Leader Experience.

The principles of the ladders help us understand more about this miracle of God's grace, not only for our salvation, but as the basis of how we live our Christian life. For many, grace makes sense for their salvation, but is perceived as a doctrine that gives too much permission for the Christian life.

**THE
CAPACITY
LADDER**

As the rails combine to create a community of grace, several important things begin occurring. Our character is developed. Trust is built. Truth is being told. Life increasingly becomes authentic. We call this a TrueFaced life.

Consider this diagram. In this life, we who have trusted Christ will always have sin issues, and we will always have the identity God gave us. They are constants. Unchanging realities.

Working on my Sin Issues ⟶

Trusting Who God Says I Am ⟶

It's key that we ask ourselves: Which one of these two constants defines my life focus? Which offers me the hope of experiencing the other? If we opt for the top line, we will never experience the bottom line. But, if we focus on the bottom line, we will experience unparalleled transformation regarding our sin issues. It's a whole new way of seeing.

Think about this: What is spirituality? What is spiritual formation? How does my character form? Because I believe what God says is true about me? Or because I spend the rest of my life striving to become something I believe he wants me to be. Do you know what one does? One trusts. Do you know what the other does? The other traps me into performance every day of my Christian life.

Many are teaching that the way to deal with sin issues is to manage them somehow. We call those methods sin

THE CHARACTER LADDER

management theologies. In sin management theology we just want to make sure we don't mess up too badly. Or when we do, we hide. All sin management theologies are theologies of changing you. The goal in those models is that as a Christian I am finally going to change. But, sin can not be managed.

Draw an arrow from "Trusting who God says I am" up to "Working on my sin issues" to illustrate that trusting who God says I am will always lead me to God's ability to deal with my sin issues.

The Environment of Grace changes our life focus. It changes how we treat each other and our sin issues. Do I see my brother or my sister as a saved sinner or a saint who sins? This viewpoint changes everything about our relationships. If I see my sister in Christ as a sinner, I will always see our sin between us, and that perception of her will give me permission to walk away. But if I see her as the saint God declares her to be, a saint who I'm convinced is going to sin, I will stay in relationship.

An environment of grace is a safe, not a soft, place where my perspective on all of life begins to change. The truth of this rail represents one of the most powerful components in my spiritual development.

QUALITIES OF AN ENVIRONMENT OF GRACE

Safe, Not Soft

Protecting

Love

How we view each other

Healing

Maturing vs. Changing

Releasing – Person/Potential

Influence –Pursuing/Receiving Power

Creative, Productive

Dependent on God/Others

Identity-Living out of who God says we are

Freedom-God is the resource not the last resort to deal with sin

Relationships of Trust

Truth-Telling

Serious About Sin

Light – An Unhidden Place

Intimate, Authentic, Committed

Gifts of Grace

　　-Repentance

　　-Forgiveness

Focused Mission

Accepting

Humility

Submission

Permission

Effective, Productive

Vulnerable

Trusting Truth

Fulfilled

RELATIONSHIPS OF TRUST

Without the rails I have no safe place
- to tell the truth.
- to develop emotional maturity.
- to be protected from my own destructive tendencies.
- to build character.

Character is developed in _____,
but it is _____ in isolation.

All character words are words of relationship.

Trust is a love word.
> The degree to which I trust you is the degree to which you can love me, no matter how much love you have for me.

Integrity is that quality of _____ that _____
from _____.

Relationships of trust free us to receive and give love.

Love is the process of meeting needs.

Trusting you to meet my needs.
- I must acknowledge that I have needs.
- You desire to meet one of my needs with an expression of your love.
- I must then choose to let you meet my needs.
- When my needs are met, I am fulfilled.

Affirmation is a _____ that God
designed in me.

> ▶ Affirmation is a love word that ministers to the
> heart. It is an honest appreciation for who we
> are, what we do and what we mean to others.

Its motivation is for the benefit of the one affirmed.
Affirmation gives to give, unlike manipulation, which
gives to get.

"Let another praise you and not your own mouth."
        Proverbs 27:2

That "letting" is the trusting.

Affirmation may involve correcting my theology and
vocabulary.

> ▶ Affirmation is love and love does not inflame
> sin.
> ▶ Critical attitudes and words diminish in a
> community of affirmation.

Affirmation . . .

> ▶ Clarifies my _____
>
> ▶ Reinforces my _____
>
> ▶ Develops my _____
>
> ▶ Heals my _____

**THE
CHARACTER
LADDER**

RELATIONSHIPS OF TRUST

It's not easy to grow up. Without those rails that integrate my life-environments of grace and relationships of trust-I have no safe place to grow up—to mature. God calls us to be in relationship with each other. If I've lived in a family or worked a long time in organizations where the environment is performance-obsessed or law-based, I will remain immature.

Without the rails, I have no safe place to tell the truth or to develop emotional maturity. When I'm not in a safe place and a crisis happens, I become the issue rather than the real issue being the focus. This is why we say without the rails, I have no safe place to be protected from my own destructive tendencies or to build character. I need people to walk alongside of me, to lovingly help me see me, to trust them with me, to let them protect me.

Shallow relationships don't require much of us, and they don't reveal much of us. We need deep, intimate relationships of trust so our character can develop.

Character is developed in relationships, but revealed or tested in isolation. All character words are words of relationship. Humility, submission, love, integrity, and so forth can only develop and function in relationship.

THE CHARACTER LADDER

The reason relationships of trust are fundamental is that trust is the doorway to love. If you trust no one but yourself, others cannot love you. They can inform you that they love you, but they cannot love you until you trust their love. Notice how trust and love are related: The degree to which I trust you is the degree to which you can love me no matter how much love you have for me. If you have abundant love for me, but my walls are high and thick, no matter how much love you have for me, I'll never experience your love. All I'll know is self-protection—which is an oxymoron.

That is why integrity is crucial to relationships. Integrity is that quality of character that elicits trust from others. When I have integrity, you trust me. When you have integrity, I trust you.

Therefore, your integrity is essential for people to experience your love. If they trust you, they will experience your love. Relationships of trust free us to receive and give love.

Love is the process of meeting needs. All processes have sequences. This is the sequence of love: First, I must acknowledge that I have needs. Genesis 2:18 demonstrates that before sin entered the world, Adam had needs. Not because of sin, but because God designed Adam with limitations. Those limitations created needs, that others such as Eve could fill. Adam had a need for relationships. God knows what our needs are. He created them.

After I acknowledge that I have needs, you express a desire to meet one of my needs with an expression

3

RELATIONSHIPS OF TRUST

of your love, your strength. Third, I must then choose to let you meet my needs. That letting is the trust I place in you. Then, when I trust I will receive your love! And, when my needs are met, I am fulfilled.

One of the most significant ways for us to experience love is through one of our God–designed needs—a need called affirmation. Affirmation is a love word that ministers to the heart. It's an honest appreciation for who we are, what we do, and what we mean to others.

Affirmation's motivation is for the benefit of the one affirmed. Affirmation gives to give, unlike manipulation which gives to get.

Proverbs 27 states a very important principle about affirmation. Let another praise (affirm) you and not your own mouth. For those who have a difficult time trusting others, affirmation is a great way to begin to let someone in. It's a starting point in beginning to trust others with you. Because when someone affirms you, you know they're for you. You know they appreciate you, and they know you! It's an awesome thing.

But you may have an experience in your history where you were taught that it's not good to affirm people, because that will inflame sin or pride in them. Or, worse yet, you may be from a situation where the intention of that person was to keep you humble by criticizing you or withholding praise from you. If this is true for you, affirmation may involve correcting your theology and your vocabulary.

Affirmation is a love word. And, love does not inflame sin. You will notice that critical attitudes and words diminish in a community of affirmation.

Affirmation clarifies my identity. Those who are not affirmed lose a piece of their identity. Affirmation reinforces my confidence. There's not nearly as much questioning and doubting who God has made me to be. Affirmation develops my character as I learn to trust what others say is true about me. It also inspires me to live to up to the character they have seen in my life. Finally, affirmation heals my wounds.

3 RELATIONSHIPS OF TRUST

NOTES

_____

_____

_____

_____

_____

_____

_____

_____

_____

_____

_____

_____

_____

**THE
CHARACTER
LADDER**

HUMILITY

The rails begin materializing as I step on the first rung.

Environments of Grace:

Living out of who God says I am

Relationships of Trust:

The degree to which I trust you . . .

God opposes the proud, but he gives grace to the humble.

Therefore, humility _____ God's
_____.

Grace is always unmerited, but it is not always uninitiated.

Humility is _____ God and others with
_____.

Relational Evidences of Humility

How I view _____   Believing how those I
                            trust _____ me

How I _____ others   Believing others _____
                            me

How I let others _____   Believing I can
to me   _____ to others

I cannot claim _____ before God if I do not let your
_____, _____, and _____ affect
who I am becoming.

Many leaders expect their colleagues and subordinates to trust
them, but have no intention of trusting anyone with themselves.

Many leaders demand trust out of position or power.

Others realize they must earn trust.

Few realize that to earn trust, one must first _____
trust.

Humility leads to:

> ▸ Contributing my strengths to benefit others.

> ▸ Submitting to the strengths of others for my benefit.

HUMILITY

The ladder of influence is held together and integrated by two rails, relationships of trust and these environments of grace. It is a ladder of humility to exaltation, whose rungs and rails are illustrated in Philippians 2.

"Have this mind among yourselves which is yours in Christ Jesus. Who though he was in the form of God did not count equality with God a thing to be grasped, but made himself nothing, taking the form of a servant, being born in the likeness of men. And being found in human form, he humbled himself by becoming obedient to the point of death, even death on the cross. Therefore, God hath highly exalted and bestowed on him the name that is above every name, so that at the name of Jesus every knee should bow in heaven and on earth and under the earth, and every tongue confess that Jesus Christ is Lord, to the glory of God the Father." Philippians 2.

Jesus is our model for understanding how we mature, how we develop from the inside out. How do we understand how our character is formed? There is a fascinating give and take between three pieces of this ladder, the two rails and the first rung. The first rung is humility and you'll notice that we believe "The rails begin materializing as I step on the first rung." These two rails called the environment of grace and relationships of trust are disconnected until you start to build the ladder, and that requires humility.

Humility is trusting God and others with me. Humility

is trusting what God says is true about me. When trust is active in me it empowers others around to trust me, it inspires trust in them and in our relationships. This is when the second rail begins to show up or develop—the relationships of trust. This rail becomes critical for living out the mark of Christianity in my relationships: receiving love from others and offering love to others. The degree to which I trust you is the degree to which you can love me no matter how much love you have for me.

With a pen or pencil draw a triangle that connects these three components of the ladder: these two rails, relationships of trust and environments of grace, along with the first rung humility. Without humility, we will not live well in community with each other. Without humility, we will not experience relationships of trust. Without humility, we will not receive love from others.

THE CHARACTER LADDER

Therefore, as part of our foundation for the Christian life, one of the attributes that we want to learn well is the reality of how important humility is to the healing, maturing and influence of our lives. Foundational to the development of my person is understanding humility.

Consider I Peter 5. God opposes a certain kind of person—the proud. Yet, He gives grace to another kind of person—a humble person. This is a supreme principle.

Humility is paramount, because humility attracts God's grace. Grace is the means by which we have relationship with God. Grace is the means by which God has relationship with us. Think through this next statement: God depends on the work of Jesus Christ to have a relationship with you, as much as you depend on the work of Jesus Christ to have a relationship with Him. We must believe that dependency on grace is as important to live the Christian life as it is for the sinner to become saved.

So, what is humility, this quality that attracts God's grace?

Luke 18:9. "Jesus told this parable to some who trusted in themselves." That's his audience. The proud are those who trust in themselves for righteousness. "Two men went into the temple to pray, one a Pharisee the other a tax collector. The Pharisee standing by himself (praying to himself) prayed, 'God, I thank you that I am not like other men – an extortioner, unjust, adulterer, or even like this man over here. And besides, I fast twice a week, I give tithes of all I get. But the tax collector standing far off would not even lift his eyes to heaven, but beat his breast saying God be merciful to me a sinner." Jesus said, "I tell you this man went down to his house justified rather than the other, for everyone who exalts himself will be humbled, but the one who humbles himself will be exalted."

I Peter 5 is telling us that while grace is always unmerited, it is not always uninitiated. You can never earn grace, but we can spurn grace—we can turn it away. We define humility as trusting God and others with whom? With that definition, why do you think humility is so hard for us to get our hearts around, because we want to be what? In control.

So this is the sequence: Without trust, we can't experience love. Without humility, we will not trust. The relational evidence of humility is in how I view you. And then believing how those I trust view me. That's how I know that I am expressing and experiencing humility.

A second way that we can know we are maturing in our understanding of humility is being able to make a heart statement about how I actually need others, and then believing that others need me.

Never confuse humility with a bad opinion of yourself.
To say that no one needs you is not humility. It's just a
bad opinion of yourself. Humility says that I am by the
grace of God, gifted. I am by the grace of God, growing
up. The third relational evidence of humility is demon-
strated in how well I let others minister to me and
believing I can minister to others.

An excellent summary of these statements is that I cannot claim humility before God if I do not let your
affirmation, guidance, and love affect who I am becoming. The challenge for many leaders is that they expect
their colleagues and subordinates to trust them, but have
no intention of trusting anyone with themselves.

Many leaders demand trust out of position. Others realize
they must earn trust. Yet, few realize that to earn trust one
must first learn trust. This is the Philippians 2 lesson.

Humility leads to many relational benefits. Here are
two powerful outcomes: Contributing my strengths
to benefit others and submitting to the strengths of
others for my benefit. That's a process. A process of
humility. Attempt to climb this ladder without
attention to the rails and to humility and we will
move right back into performance-driven sin management practices. So, if I want to as a person
develop a culture of grace where safety, truth, and
character abound then I must begin with the essence
of humility: Trusting God and others with me.

SUBMISSION

Submission is a _____ word.

- Without trust, I cannot practice humility.
- Without humility, I cannot practice submission.
- Without submission, I will not experience your influence in my life.

Vulnerability is a practical application of submission.

Vulnerability is the result of coming under another's influence.

- In relationships, vulnerability does not _____ to transparency.
- Transparency has value, but it is limited.
- Selective transparency is a clever means of remaining isolated.

Vulnerability both expresses and sustains my integrity.

- Vulnerability triggers a two-way relational effect.
    First, people gain access to me.
    Second, I am given access to them,
        as they trust me.

- This kind of relationship is _____.

5
SUBMISSION

Vulnerability expands productivity and influence.

▶ Influence is based on trust.
▶ Trust is based on integrity.
▶ Integrity is sustained in vulnerability.

Trust does not lead to vulnerability, so much as vulnerability leads to trust.

THE CHARACTER LADDER

SUBMISSION

THE CHARACTER LADDER

5 SUBMISSION

Rung two on this character ladder is submission. First rung was what? Humility. And we're up to this rung of submission. Remember that this ladder is rooted in Philippians 2 and other scriptures, eg. Hebrews 12, I Peter 5, "Humble yourself under the mighty hand of God, that in due time, He can exalt you" and take you to rung 5, the rung of destiny, the rung of exaltation. So we are looking at a very interesting rung, probably not the most popular rung in this culture. Submission.

Submission is a relationship word. In session 3 we said, "Submission is a love word." Submission is also a relationship word. It is also a word that relates us to one another. Without trust, I really can't practice humility. I can practice other things that look like humility, but without trust I can't get to the core of humility. And then without humility, I can't practice submission. I might be able to practice compliance, that looks like submission, but without humility I can't come under another person's influence.

Therefore, without this submission I won't experience their influence in my life. I'll be limited to my own strengths which have great limitations. In addition to that, I will have weaknesses that complicate my strengths. So, if I don't let that submission that's driven by humility, which is driven by trust, actually flower in my life, then I will not know your influence, your protection in my life. That's how this submission is related to these other words.

So, we talk about this word, vulnerability. Vulnerability is a practical application of submission. It's not everything that submission is, but it's a practical application of submission. Vulnerability, is the result of coming under another person's influence.

Transparency has value. It's good to be transparent. But the value is limited. In fact, the tricky part about this is that often times the more articulate or eloquent people are, the better they are at selective transparency. And so this truth of vulnerability going beyond the good thing of transparency is so important, and it's linked inseparably to submission. It's a practical outworking. So, vulnerability is the result of coming under another's influence.

Vulnerability also expresses and sustains my integrity. Vulnerability triggers a two-way relational effect. First, people gain access to me, and then because they can begin to trust me, this is not a game, they begin to give access to themselves. This kind of relationship is called authentic. Many people teach authenticity, but very few get to live it because this is the uncommon path to authenticity. And many people, when they look at vulnerability and giving permission, will say, "No, I know what vulnerability means, it means at risk, exposed, unsafe. I'm gonna take a pass on vulnerability." Do you know what they give up? Authenticity, spiritual formation, protection, and the strengths of others. They also give up that influence that would come in a whole variety of ways. This is so important to leader development.

If I learn that vulnerability is the result of coming under another, and that it both sustains and expresses integrity, then I get this third powerful piece. And that is, that vulnerability expands productivity and influence. How does that work?

Let's start with influence first. Influence, remember is based on trust. That trust is based on integrity, and now

149

we observe that integrity is sustained, and built, and nurtured in vulnerability. That's why if you work it all the way back up, why you can see influence expanding. There is this beautiful verse in Ecclesiastes 4 that says, "It's better to have a poor but wise youth than an old but foolish king who no longer knows how to seek correction." That's the way so many leaders lead today. They don't grow up, they just get old.

Trust does not lead to vulnerability so much as vulnerability leads to trust. Vulnerability will issue out of submission and it will find its fruit in this whole process of giving people permission in your life.

Don't wait until you have this heart full of trust, or until you have some perfect people around you to trust, because you will have to wait until heaven for this, you will have to die first. That's not the way this works. You don't just drum up your trust, and then somehow you learn to grant permission, no! Take a step. This is only the second rung, but for some of us this feels way too high already on this ladder. I promise you that permission, that vulnerability action, leads to expanded trust. Take a step on that rung.

NOTES

OBEDIENCE

THE CHARACTER LADDER

Obedience is an expression of

_____.

- God tests our righteousness.
- Satan tempts our sinfulness.
- God trusts the obedient with truth.

Obedience is not compliance.
- Compliance hinders _____.
- Compliance is limited to the _____ of others.
- Compliance creates _____.
- Others are held responsible for my life choices.

Obeying is trusting.

Obedience does not initiate, but is a response to God's initiative.

My response is to obey God. His responsibility is to protect me and take responsibility for the consequence of my obedience.

Trusting truth is the basis for spiritual formation, God's intended process for our maturing.
- Truth _____ only when it is trusted.

OBEDIENCE

Let's review the first two rungs as we prepare to ascend to the third rung. The principles we are learning are critical to our spiritual health and well-being. They are the core principles of our spiritual identity, maturity and destiny.

In order for my character to be formed, I need God and I need you. Without this foundation of humility–trusting God and others with me–my character is not going to be formed well.

Isolation creates a distance from others, and in that distance I have an inability to clearly see truth.

Submission is critical as a next step in a process of my character being formed. If I say that I trust someone with me, I can demonstrate that is true when I intentionally come under their influence. Until I intentionally come under this influence, I have not yet validated the trust I say I have in them. It's one thing for us to say, "I think I got it now, trusting God with me, yeah I got it, I got it memorized." Well, I haven't got the humility until I begin to move toward you with submission and come under your influence. I let you speak into who I am. I let you love me. That letting you speak into who I am is processing submission together.

There are some deep roots that create for us unhealthiness. One of the roots that creates for me unhealthiness is when you choose to sin against me. But another deep root that creates unhealthiness in

THE CHARACTER LADDER

OBEDIENCE **6**

me is when you choose not to love me. Unloved people are severely distorted in who they really are. If I say that I trust God with me, and if I say that I would love to submit to the will of God in my life, I will demonstrate that humble, submissive spirit by acting upon the influence of God. That's what obedience is–aligning with truth. Obedience is acting upon the instruction, the love and the encouragement of the Word of God. It's acting upon it!

Without submission, we will never practice obedience. And without humility, we will never practice submission. These words represent critical principles. God gives grace to the humble! And when in trust I intentionally let God influence my life, I will demonstrate I am doing that by acting upon that influence. That's called obedience.

The first line is foundational to our understanding of obedience. Obedience is an expression of our righteousness. The righteous are the ones who obey because they are righteous.

In James chapter 1, God, does what? Tests our righteousness. Satan does what? He tempts our sinfulness. God tests our righteousness. Meaning this – God gives us opportunities in which we can demonstrate that we are righteous. How would we do that? By obeying him, thus doing the right thing, aligning with truth. So what does Satan do? He wants to tempt our sinfulness. In Genesis 39, Joseph was tempted by Potiphar's wife. He said no. Now, Satan was tempting the potential of Joseph's sinfulness while God was testing his righteousness. They are not mutually exclusive. In the very same incident where I have an opportunity to be tempted to sin, I am also a Christian in that opportunity,

6
OBEDIENCE

being tested in righteousness. God never tempts me with sin, but He tests me to prove that I am what? Righteous.

God trusts the obedient with truth. The reason we obey is not to receive a blessing, that is not the reason for obedience. Joseph did not get blessed as a result of the testing of his righteousness, his act of obedience. He got to go to prison for a couple of years.

When we are obedient, we may not receive a blessing, but we will always receive a promise. God will not forsake us! When we act obediently as a result of trusting God with who we are, God then trusts us with truth.

Obedience is not compliance. Compliance is not obedience. Compliance hinders our productivity, it hinders our effectiveness. Compliance is limited to the expectations of others. Compliance creates immaturity where others are held responsible for my life choices. Compliance says, "I will do what I have to do to please you." Or, "I will do what I have to do to live up to the expectations you have for me." But every time I act in compliance, I will hold you responsible for my choices.

Obedience does not initiate. It is a response to God's initiative. You and I do not create the opportunity to really tell God, "God, look what I'm gonna do for you." God would like to show us what He would do for us. In I Samuel 15, Saul was to eliminate the Amalekites, but he kept the king. And he let the people keep the sheep and the oxen. For what? For a sacrifice. "When Samuel the prophet came to Saul later, he said to Saul, "Why did you not obey the Lord?" And Saul's response was, "I did, I did obey the Lord." I did obey the best I could, that's what I did! I gave God my best! I killed all of them except the king, and if it wasn't for the people, they're the reason all these sheep are here.

God does not want our best. He wants our trust of Him, so He can give us His best. It's that critical a verse in scripture to help us understand God's heart. I Samuel 15:22 in the Old Testament carries the priority of a John 3:16 in the New Testament. "Has the Lord as great delight in burnt offering and sacrifices as in obeying the voice of the Lord? Behold, to obey is better than sacrifice." This is a critical, pivotal point in the Bible to lay a foundation for our understanding of our relationship with God. To obey is better than sacrifice. Unless I trust God with me, I won't obey him. It is easier for people to sacrifice for God than it is for people to obey him.

My response is to obey God. His responsibility is to protect me and take responsibility for the consequences of my obedience. The story of the three young men in Daniel describes how they were given the opportunity to go into the fiery furnace. "We don't know what God's going to do. We may die. But if we die, He is still God and we trust him." And we trust him. This powerful concept of trust causes me to be a person who desires to obey God.

Trusting truth is the basis for spiritual formation, which is God's intended process for our maturing. I Peter 1:22. "Having purified your souls by your obedience to the truth, for a sincere brotherly love,

6 OBEDIENCE

love one another from a pure heart." Trusting truth is the basis for spiritual formation. It's the basis for spiritual formation. Truth transforms when it is trusted.

Our goal is to stop accumulating more knowledge, so we can start obeying the truth within the knowledge we already have. When we learn to obey the truth in the knowledge we already have, it means we're trusting that truth, and that is what spiritually transforms.

NOTES

SUFFERING

THE CHARACTER LADDER

This is a suffering unique to the Christian.

▶ The mature suffer for others'_____
so they can _____, standing
firm in their faith.

Suffering involves taking risk for relational opportunities, just as others have previously risked for me.

Suffering is the result of humbly choosing to implement the love, truth and guidance I have already experienced, but now, for the benefit of those I influence.

Choices of obedience rooted in humility and identity keep us objective (focused) in the process of suffering.

The purpose of the character development process (humility, submission, and obedience) is to prepare the leader for suffering not _____.

Two cautions:

▶ Suffering is not focusing on things being lost.
▶ Suffering is not endured so blessings can be received.

7

SUFFERING

SUFFERING

I Peter 2:20, I Peter 3:13 and I Peter 4:12 "For what credit is it if, when you sin and are beaten for it, you endure it? But if when you do good and suffer for it and endure it, this is a gracious thing in the sight of God. For to this you have been called."

There is a suffering unique to the Christian. There is suffering that all of us know that is common to humanity. We all can have heart attacks, terminal illness, accidents. just like non-Christians. We have cancer. This is not the suffering that is unique to the Christian. The suffering that's unique to the Christian is the suffering that comes as a result of humbly submitting to God and, in obedience, following the instruction and encouragement of God in a world that doesn't like Him very much. In fact, He said the world would hate us. One of the reasons many Christians get lazy about obedience is that they innately know this truth. Obedience can take us into places that may be very uncomfortable for us, as we, like our Lord, suffer for doing good. That is obedience and suffering.

A healthy local church gathers to be nurtured together because they are out in the world suffering. An unhealthy local church has no "out there" expression. When a church has no out there expression, the saints are not suffering this kind of suffering. They're just grieving over the common suffering known to people. The mature suffer for other's joy. So they can mature. Ultimately standing firm in their faith.

**THE
CHARACTER
LADDER**

One of the ways that we can in fact experience suffering is when because of humility we become others-oriented. And when we become others-oriented, and many of the others that we want to be committed to can be pretty immature in their Christian life. Immature Christians can become a real handful.

Suffering involves taking risks for relational opportunities, just as others have previously risked for me. It's a suffering that takes risks intentionally for someone else's well-being.

Suffering is a result of humbly choosing to implement the love, truth, and guidance I have already experienced, but now for the benefit of those I influence.

Choices of obedience rooted in humility and identity keep us objective or focused in the process of suffering. Suffering is hard. Read Paul's account in II Corinthians. Read what he suffered. When we are able to trust God because we are humble, our perspective on suffering will always be right. It doesn't mean it doesn't hurt. It hurt Paul to be beaten, and to be stoned and left for dead.

One of the reasons we fear suffering is because we lack humility. Because we lack trusting God with who we are, therefore we fear suffering. Paul actually wanted to fellowship in the sufferings of Jesus Christ.

The purpose of the character development process, humility, submission, and obedience is to prepare the leader for suffering, not isolation. The character

7

SUFFERING

development process does not create for us an isolated relationship with God! The character
development process is not a vertical experience
only. The character development process is to prepare us for suffering, which means to prepare us to
engage in good in this world and in those who are
younger than us so that they may grow up. That is
this suffering.

Suffering is not focusing on things being lost! The
pursuit is not suffering. The pursuit is obedience,
the consequence of which may be suffering. If you
pursue suffering, you will be spiritually unhealthy.

Suffering is never to be focused on the things I gave
up for Jesus. Paul said what? He counted them all
as garbage. Philippians 3:7-11

Second, suffering is not endured so blessings can be
received. Ask Jeremiah this when you get to heav-
en. Do not pursue suffering. When in fact we
trust God with who we are we come under his
influence, and we obey him, which takes us into
opportunities to do good and where we do good,
we will suffer. Then the purposes of God for our
lives will be realized. That is why exaltation is the
next step.

DESTINY

God's goal for us is never just healing, safety, rest or even receiving multiple benefits . . . his goal is for us to be _____ into his dreams for us, our destiny, our influence.

In grace we learn to trust, to wait, to rest in God's promises to mature in authentic relationships as we move toward his destiny for our lives.

Our influence is dependent on whether we learn to _____ rather than _____ power.

The mature own the influence of their person, in:
- Delighting in the success of others.
- Searching for ways to care for and improve the circumstances of others.
- Benefiting _____ their team and community.

8
DESTINY

▶ _____ for and in the
consequences of paying the price for decisions
of integrity.

What are the challenges in living for the benefit
of those you influence?

**THE
CHARACTER
LADDER**

DESTINY 8

DESTINY

THE CHARACTER LADDER

We have a chance through our influence to make a significant difference in this world. What we need to do is concentrate on trusting God (that's called humility) so that we are able with submission to come under his influence, so that we are able then to obey him. In that obedience will be able to endure the reality of what it is like to be like Jesus in this world. Out of that reality will come our destiny, a clearer understanding of the call of God on our lives.

Our destiny is about owning our influence. It's making life choices based upon the convictions we have.

Destiny moves us from a casual Christianity to a life of conviction. What would it mean for you to own your influence?

This fifth rung is not something you step up onto. In this way, it is unlike the previous four rungs. You don't step up onto the exaltation rung, God brings you to it.

Trusting God will move us into arenas that are more significant than our potential and greater than our goals. God does not want us to live to the limit of our potential, but to the limit of His testimony for us.

I Peter 5:5,6 "God is opposed to the proud, but gives grace to the humble." "Humble yourselves under the mighty hand of God and he will exalt

8
DESTINY

you in due time." Do not pursue your destiny, pursue humility and you will reach your destiny. When Jesus said to those disciples, "Follow me and I'll make you become fishers of men," they at that point had to make a choice of trust and decision, which they later grew into. They matured into that decision of trust. But without those choices of trust, we will never mature.

God's goal for us is never just healing, safety, rest, or even receiving multiple benefits. His goal is for us to be released into his dreams for us, our destiny, our influence.

In order for the local church to be healthy, it must be a place where we dream and where we get in touch with God's dreams for us. It must be a place where we are released into those dreams, where there is a celebration of our being able to be blessed with a conviction that this is what God has called us to do.

In grace, we learn to trust, to wait, to rest in God's promises, to mature in authentic relationships as we move toward his destiny for our lives. It is not possible to move into God's dream for your life without authentic relationships because authentic relationships are the evidence of your humility.

God wants our humility, so He can give us his excellence. *Our* excellence and the pursuit of it will stand in the way of receiving God's excellence. God wants our trust, so he can give us his best. This is never an excuse, never, to be slothful, lazy, and indifferent.

Our influence is dependent on whether we learn to receive rather than pursue power. The pursuit of

DESTINY 8

power, (authority) will always make us vulnerable to the power we pursue. And eventually, we will abuse that power, and the process will abuse us.

Authority is something we want to receive from the Lord. Joseph is a great biblical example of a person with humility who endured prison, and with humility was able to receive from Pharaoh, power second only to Pharaoh in all of Egypt. At the time he ruled Egypt, it was the most powerful nation on the Earth, but he never sat in the prison trying to figure out how to become second in command in Egypt.

Moses is a good example of someone who misunderstood this statement. Once Moses realized he was a Jew, Moses wanted to take on the responsibility, by the authority of his adopted role as Pharaoh's son, to release the persecutions of the Jews. So he killed somebody. Not a good plan.

Receiving power is the ability to be appointed of God to a significant place of authority and never be ruined by that position. Without humility, power will in fact destroy you, position will destroy you.

Romans teaches us that all authority, all positions of authority are delegated by God. Biblically, all authority roles are for the benefit of those that are influenced by that role. In the Bible, the purpose of the role, is for the benefit of those that are influenced, whether that's a husband or a mother or an elder or a boss or a king. The motivation in pursuing power is self-benefit, no matter how well we mask it. The motivation in receiving power is other people's benefit, and that cannot come without humility.

8

DESTINY

The mature own their influence in at least these four significant ways. They delight in the success of others; competition is not in the spirit of the humble. They search for ways to care for and improve the circumstances of others. The humble understand what it means to be a servant. As servants they really do care, as Philippians would teach us, in putting the needs of others above their own.

The mature own their influence in choosing to benefit with their team and community. As we have taught in other places, isolation is the greatest cause of dysfunction in leaders. The humble benefit *with* their team not *at the expense* of their team or apart from their team. The mature suffer and pay the price for decisions of integrity. As Paul wisely teaches, to join in the sufferings of Jesus Christ is not a penalty but a blessing, but only the humble would ever believe that is true.

DESTINY 8

CHARACTER AND CAPACITY

Are you the kind of person who others want to follow or *have* to follow?

Roles are essential in organizations, but the ultimate influence of your life will come more from <u>who you are</u> than even <u>what you do.</u>

Leading from this influence requires a special quality that leading from position or power does not: Trust.

Influence is based on trust and this trust is anchored in two components: Character and Capacity.

Surveys from business, education, government and military indicate that the quality with the greatest gap between what followers most want in their leaders and what they actually receive is Trust.

We call this The Trust Gap.

Most people discover their lives are like the Capacity Ladder.

At the top of the Capacity Ladder are stressors and strains one never experienced at the bottom:

Pressure of <u>success</u>	Drain of <u>critics</u>
Temptation of <u>privilege</u>	Isolation of <u>leadership</u>
Demands of <u>followers</u>	

These capacity rungs are important to personal development, but when character is assumed it leads to <u>disintegration</u> of the ladders (of life).

A disintegrated life results in:

Relational Struggles	Lost Opportunities
Emotional Immaturity	Failure and Falling

Nothing hides disintegration like success for a season.

The critical question for any person is "How do I <u>integrate</u> my life? How do I put these two ladders together?"

ENVIRONMENTS OF GRACE

The rails integrate the ladders.

The rails are the missing components in many spiritual development programs today.

The rails combine to create a community of grace, where
>   Character is developed.
>   Trust is built.
>   Truth is told.
>   Life is authentic (truefaced).

The Environment of Grace changes our life focus:

Working on my Sin Issues
————————————————————————————➤

Trusting who God says I am
————————————————————————————➤

How I view me may be the most revealing commentary of my theology.

The Qualities of an Environment of Grace.

Grace changes how we treat each other and our sin issues.

A saved sinner or a saint who sins.

RELATIONSHIPS OF TRUST

Without the rails I have no safe place to tell the truth, to develop emotional maturity, to be protected from my own destructive tendencies, to build character.

Character is developed in <u>relationship</u>, but it is <u>tested</u> in isolation.

All character words are words of relationship.

Trust is a love word.

The degree to which I trust you is the degree to which you can love me, no matter how much love you have for me.

Integrity is that quality of <u>character</u> that <u>elicits trust</u> from <u>others</u>.

Relationships of trust free us to receive and give love.

Love is the process of meeting needs.

Trusting you to meet my needs.
> I must acknowledge that I have needs.
> You desire to meet one of my needs with an expression of your love.
> I must then choose to let you meet my needs.
> When my needs are met, I am fulfilled.

Affirmation is a <u>need</u> that God designed in me.

Affirmation is a love word that ministers to the heart. It is an honest appreciation for who we are, what we do and what we mean to others.

Its motivation is for the benefit of the one affirmed.

Affirmation gives to give, unlike manipulation, which gives to get.

"Let another praise you and not your own mouth." Proverbs 27:2

> That "letting" is the trusting.

Affirmation may involve correcting my theology and vocabulary.
> Affirmation is love and love does not inflame sin.
> Critical attitudes and words diminish in a community of affirmation.

Affirmation . . .
> Clarifies my <u>identity</u>, reinforces my <u>confidence</u>, develops my <u>character</u>, and heals my <u>wounds</u>.

HUMILITY

The rails begin materializing as I step on the first rung.

Environments of Grace: Living out of who God says I am

Relationships of Trust: The degree to which I trust you . . .

God opposes the proud, but he gives grace to the humble.

Therefore, humility <u>attracts</u> God's <u>grace</u>.

Grace is always unmerited, but it is not always uninitiated.

Humility is <u>trusting</u> God and others with <u>me</u>.

Relational Evidences of Humility

How I view <u>others</u>	Believing how those I trust <u>view</u> me
How I <u>need</u> others	Believing others <u>need</u> me
How I let others <u>minister</u> to me	Believing I can <u>minister</u> to others

I cannot claim <u>humility</u> before God if I do not let your <u>affirmation</u>, <u>guidance</u>, and <u>love</u> affect who I am becoming.

Many leaders expect their colleagues and subordinates to trust them, but have no intention of trusting anyone with themselves.

Many leaders demand trust out of position or power.

Others realize they must earn trust.

Few realize that to earn trust, one must first <u>learn</u> trust.

Humility leads to:

> Contributing my strengths to benefit others.
> Submitting to the strengths of others for my benefit.

SUBMISSION

Submission is a <u>relationship</u> word.

> Without trust, I cannot practice humility.
> Without humility, I cannot practice submission.
> Without submission, I will not experience your influence in my life.

Vulnerability is a practical application of submission.

Vulnerability is the result of coming under another's influence.

> In relationships, vulnerability does not <u>equate</u> to transparency.
>
> Transparency has value, but it is limited.
>
> Selective transparency is a clever means of remaining isolated.

Vulnerability both expresses and sustains my integrity.

> Vulnerability triggers a two-way relational effect.
>> First, people gain access to me.
>> Second, I am given access to them, as they trust me.
>
> This kind of relationship is <u>authentic</u>.

Vulnerability expands productivity and influence.

> Influence is based on trust.
> Trust is based on integrity.
> Integrity is sustained in vulnerability.

Trust does not lead to vulnerability, so much as vulnerability leads to trust.

OBEDIENCE

Obedience is an expression of <u>righteousness.</u>

> God tests our righteousness.
>
> Satan tempts our sinfulness.
>
> God trusts the obedient with truth.

Obedience is not compliance.

> Compliance hinders <u>productivity</u>.
>
> Compliance is limited to the <u>expectations</u> of others.
>
> Compliance creates <u>immaturity.</u>
>
> Others are held responsible for my life choices.

Obeying is trusting.

Obedience does not initiate, but is a response to God's initiative.

My response is to obey God. His responsibility is to protect me and take responsibility for the consequence of my obedience.

Trusting truth is the basis for spiritual formation, God's intended process for our maturing.

Truth <u>transforms</u> only when it is trusted.

SUFFERING

This is a suffering unique to the Christian.

> The mature suffer for others' <u>joy</u> so they can <u>mature</u>, standing firm in their faith.

Suffering involves taking risk for relational opportunities, just as others have previously risked for me.

Suffering is the result of humbly choosing to implement the love, truth and guidance I have already experienced, but now, for the benefit of those I influence.

Choices of obedience rooted in humility and identity keep us objective (focused) in the process of suffering.

The purpose of the character development process (humility, submission, and obedience) is to prepare the leader for suffering not <u>isolation</u>.

Two cautions:

> Suffering is not focusing on things being lost.
>
> Suffering is not endured so blessings can be received.

DESTINY

God's goal for us is never just healing, safety, rest or even receiving multiple benefits . . . his goal is for us to be <u>released</u> into his dreams for us, our destiny, our influence.

In grace we learn to trust, to wait, to rest in God's promises to mature in authentic relationships as we move toward his destiny for our lives.

Our influence is dependent on whether we learn to <u>receive</u> rather than <u>pursue</u> power.

The mature own the influence of their person, in:

> Delighting in the success of others.

> Searching for ways to care for and improve the circumstances of others.

> Benefiting <u>with</u> their team and community.

> <u>Suffering</u> for and in the consequences of paying the price for decisions of integrity.

What are the challenges in living for the benefit of those you influence?

ABOUT THE AUTHORS

BILL THRALL

serves as leadership mentor for Leadership Catalyst, (LCI) and as a director on LCI's board. Prior to LCI, Bill led Open Door Fellowship in Phoenix, a church he established in 1973. Bill is also the coauthor of The *Ascent of a Leader, Beyond Your Best* (Jossey Bass), and *TrueFaced Experience Edition* (Navpress) and continues to speak to people around the world about issues of trust, mentoring, and leadership. Bill lives in Phoenix with his wife Grace. They have three children and nine grandchildren.

BRUCE McNICOL

guides Leadership Catalyst as president, combining international work experience and degrees in finance law, theology and organizational development. He is a respected teacher and mentor for both established and emerging leaders in multiple cultures and contexts. Also the coauthor of *The Ascent of a Leader, Beyond Your Best* (Jossey Bass) and *TrueFaced Experience Edition* (Navpress). Bruce is active as a speaker and mentor around the world. He lives in Phoenix with his wife Janet and their three children.

JOHN LYNCH

serves on Leadership Catalyst's staff, speaking, filming, and writing with Bill and Bruce. He is also a contributing editor to *Beyond Your Best* (Jossey Bass) and *TrueFaced Experience Edition* (Navpress). John is the teaching pastor at Open Door Fellowship, and co-founded Sharkey Productions, a drama outreach in Phoenix. He is a playwright and storyteller, and lives in Phoenix with his wife Stacey and their three children.

ABOUT LEADERSHIP CATALYST

One word has the power to catalyze greatness in an individual, an organization, or a nation: Trust.

Surveys show that trust is the #1 requirement for influence in life and leadership. But for many, trust has been hard to come by or misplaced. There is a painful Trust Gap . . . and it appears to be widening in many arenas of the church, business, education, missions, government, and even family life.

The mission of Leadership Catalyst is to build and restore trust in leaders and in those they influence. Established in 1995, Leadership Catalyst is recognized as an international resource for helping leaders learn how to develop relationships of trust and environments of grace, which build character, authenticity, vision, and influence.

Email: info@leadershipcatalyst.org
Website: www.leadershipcatalyst.org

Voice: 888-249-0700 Toll-free in North America
Voice: 602-249-7000
Fax: 602-249-0611

Address:
Leadership Catalyst
1600 E. Northern Avenue, Suite 280
Phoenix, AZ 85020

ABOUT THE CATALYST PROCESS

Leadership Catalyst offers three High Trust programs: They are High Trust Cultures™, High Trust Leaders™ and High Trust People™. Here's the key to remember: The same principles apply to all three audiences, only the delivery changes.

High Trust People™
The High Trust People™ resources are for anyone wishing to grow in health, healing, maturity, and destiny.

- Better prepare children to make wise life choices.
- Develop stronger character.
- Elevate self-worth and esteem.
- Respect and protect each person's limitations.
- Improve honesty and trust.
- Resolve disputes to reach lasting reconciliation.
- Help each other identify and pursue life purpose.

High Trust Leaders™
The High Trust Leaders™ resources are for business and professional leaders, church and para-church leaders, institutional and mission leaders, established and emerging leaders, multi-cultural and urban leaders.

- Develop high-quality, long-lasting relationships.
- Address the primary causes of leadership failure.
- Go beyond short-term conflict resolution to long-term reconciliation.
- Improve creativity and freedom to honestly express opinions and ideas.
- Enhance appreciation for unique contributions.

High Trust Cultures™
The High Trust Cultures™ process is for major organizations, churches and institutions in which the CEO makes a cultural change choice to re-shape the way people, teams and leaders are developed.

- Create dynamic teams in place of personal agendas.
- Reduce turnover and extend staff longevity.
- Increase team effectiveness and productivity.
- Expand influence with customers, partners and other organizations.
- Establish safe (not soft), truth-telling communities.

LEADERSHIP CATALYST
RESOURCES

TrueFaced Experience Guide

Workbook companion to the TrueFaced Experience Edition. This guide is designed to be used with the 2-DVD set, which provides additional content, stories and directions to lead your small group in the TrueFaced Experience.

TrueFaced Experience 2-DVD set & Leaders Handbook

2-DVD set and Leaders Handbook provide additional content, powerful TrueFaced stories and instructions to lead your small group in the Truefaced Experience.

TrueFaced Experience Edition

By Bill Thrall, Bruce McNicol, John Lynch
Completely revised edition of the best-selling book, TrueFaced, designed to facilitate group interaction and implementation of the principles when used with the 2-DVD set and the Experience Guide.

TrueFaced Experience Leader Pack

The TrueFaced Experience is changing small groups, families, marriages, churches and organizations around the world.
The Leader Pack includes:
1 TrueFaced Experience Edition Book
1 TrueFaced Experience Guide
1 TrueFaced Experience 2-DVD Set
1 TrueFaced Leaders Handbook
1 set of TrueFaced QuEW Cards

TrueFaced Experience Small Group Pack

The TrueFaced Small Group Pack includes:
8 TrueFaced Experience Edition Books
8 TrueFaced Experience Guides
1 TrueFaced Experience 2-DVD Set
1 TrueFaced Leaders Handbook
1 set of TrueFaced QuEW Cards

The Ascent of a Leader
How Ordinary Relationships Develop Extraordinary
Character and Influence
By Bill Thrall, Bruce McNicol, Ken McElrath
Hardcover, 224 pages

Beyond Your Best
Develop Your Relationships, Fulfill Your Destiny
By Bill Thrall, Ken McElrath, Bruce McNicol
Paperback, 160 pages

The Ascent of a Leader Experience Guide
This biblically based 8-session experience provides a
powerful small group process that explores the principles form the book *The Ascent of a Leader.* The Ascent
of a Leader Experience is an engaging, interactive
experience that is ideal for any size group including
marriages, small groups, mentoring relationships,
ministry teams and Sunday school classes.

The TrueFaced Message CD
An introduction to *TrueFaced* featuring
the powerful message by John Lynch.
(45 minutes)

The TrueFaced Message Cassette
An introduction to
TrueFaced featuring the
powerful message
by John Lynch.
(45 minutes)

Experiencing Affirmation in Your Marriage
Includes two booklets containing teaching and tools for
a husband and wife to experience the power of affirming
one another.

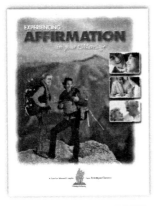

Experiencing Affirmation in Your Family
Includes four booklets
containing teaching
and tools for a family
to experience the
power of affirming
one another.
Appropriate for all
ages. (Please order one
booklet per family
member.)

Affirming Each Other-High Trust Teams™
Use this tool to experience the power of affirming
one another in your small group or team. (Please
order one tool for each team member.)

To order or for other resources and special offers,
call the Leadership Catalyst toll-free order line:
1.888.249.0700 or online:
www.leadershipcatalyst.org